groovitude

Other books by Darby Conley

The Dog Is Not a Toy (House Rule #4)

Fuzzy Logic

groovitude

A Get Fuzzy Treasury

by

Darby Conley

**Andrews McMeel
Publishing**

Kansas City

Get Fuzzy is distributed internationally by United Feature Syndicate.

Groovitude copyright © 2002 by Darby Conley. All rights reserved. Printed in China. No part of this book may be used or reproduced in any manner whatsoever without written permission except in the case of reprints in the context of reviews. For information, write Andrews McMeel Publishing, an Andrews McMeel Universal company, 4520 Main Street, Kansas City, Missouri 64111.

ISBN: 0-7407-5778-4

Get Fuzzy can be viewed on the Internet at:

www.comics.com/comics/getfuzzy

━━━━ **ATTENTION: SCHOOLS AND BUSINESSES** ━━━━

Andrews McMeel books are available at quantity discounts with bulk purchase for educational, business, or sales promotional use. For information, please write to: Special Sales Department, Andrews McMeel Publishing, 4520 Main Street, Kansas City, Missouri 64111.

Preface

Comic strips take a surprisingly long time to go from the conceptual stage to development with a syndicate to where they actually appear in newspapers. The first sketches I did of the characters that would later become Bucky, Satchel, and Rob were done in 1996. I signed a development contract in 1998, and the strip finally made it in to papers in 1999.

Now, there are two kinds of cartoonists in the world today—those who started out by ripping off *The Far Side* and those who won't admit that they've ever ripped off *The Far Side*, probably because they're still doing it (some people rip off *Calvin and Hobbes* or *Bloom County*, of course, but they all started by ripping off *The Far Side*). The first step to doing your own thing, though, is admitting your problem, which I think I did. *Get Fuzzy* was the first comic "strip" that I ever attempted, and the prospect of recurring characters and story lines forced me to do something different from the kind of *Far Side* rip-offs that I'd been doing, which is a good thing.

make fold like a collar?

Wrinkled arm too distracting ? →

I found that making a *strip* (which is different from a single panel cartoon, in that you usually have a regular cast of characters and settings and plots and a bunch of other stuff that comes with inventing a world) wasn't the most natural thing for me, though. The natural thing to do when you're an amateur cartoonist is to just think of a joke and do a little drawing that illustrates the joke. The notion that you need to focus on a few characters and give them personalities and wardrobes and relationships seemed very forced and artificial to me. Coming up with characters is a nerve-racking experience, as any cartoonist will tell you. If your comic is successful, you have to be prepared to draw the same characters for fifteen or twenty years, and that's a bit intimidating.

Given that fact, I knew that I'd need to draw talking animals to hold my interest for that long. I get bored of people, but I never get bored of animals. Especially the talking ones. As I'd only ever had a dog,

and she had been my best friend, I thought I'd want to make the main character a dog. So I started doodling dogs. "Sketching" dogs, that is. Anyway, my dog Patch was a beautiful little Border collie mix and the dogs I was drawing looked too much like her—too cute.

They were pretty and fluffy and looked more like a sappy greeting card than a comic, so I flipped through a couple of dog books to find a dog that did look funny. If you've ever seen a shar-pei, you probably realize how easy that decision was. They're almost *too* funny. Unfortunately, they're also too wrinkled to draw all the time, so Satchel underwent a process of simplifying his wrinkles. Today he pretty much looks like a shar-pei-yellow Lab cross, which is what I call him.

Cats, of course, are easier to make fun of. The cutest cat is still a freak. Where dogs are sympathetic, almost tragic, figures, cats are pure comedy. Dogs are your buddies, cats are entertainment. They're like a TV show. There's nothing funnier than when a cat falls off of something. When a dog falls down a couple of stairs, you rush to it and console it. But when a cat does it, it's funny—you point at it and laugh (which they don't like, incidentally).

So Bucky was easier to come up with. I knew that I wanted to draw a Siamese cat because 1) the white eyes popping out of his dark face and the little paws that look like gloves are funny, 2) my girlfriend has a Siamese and it's hysterical, and 3) cartoon tabbies have pretty much been done.

S'UP?

I drew a sheet of cat faces trying to find the "look" I wanted, but they all looked pretty much the same until I drew one with its ears back (a sign of aggression in cats) and it seemed so funny to me that there could be a cat in a constant state of threatening posture that I had to go with it. And the pulled-back ears, as much as any idea I had of how I'd wanted to develop the personality of the cat, dictated that Bucky's personality would be slightly hostile.

MAY I HAVE A SODA?

CAN I HAVE A COKE?

Ultimately, then, Satchel and Bucky have almost become stereotypes of "cat" and "dog"—Satchel being sweet and naïve and Bucky being selfish, and temperamental.

And I don't want to say Rob was an afterthought, because he was named after two of my best friends (both conveniently named Rob), but essentially he was. He is the straight man—the vehicle that gives Bucky and Satchel context. Bucky's not nearly as funny, it turns out, unless he's annoying somebody . . .

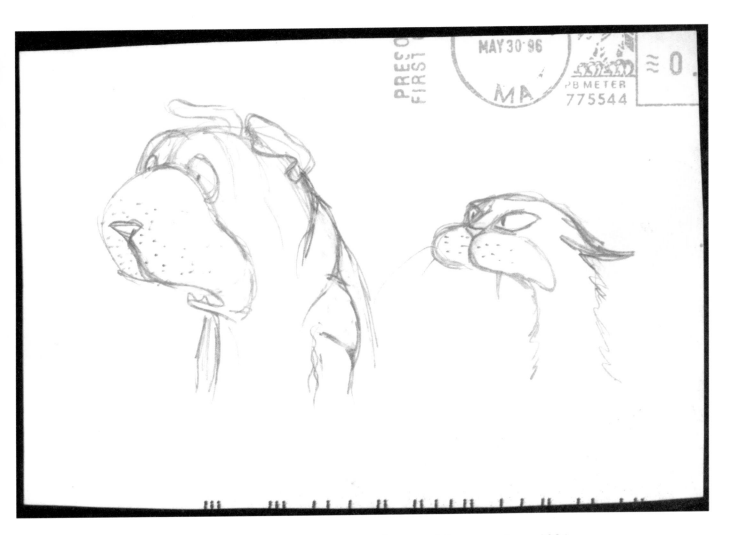

Colorplate 1. DARBY CONLEY. *Il cane ed il protagonista.* 1996.
Graphite on Envelope, $3^{1}/_{4}$ x $4^{3}/_{4}$".
Private Collection, Boston

YOU KNOW, MY PET BUG NEVER DOES **ANYTHING**.

SATCHEL, YOUR "PET BUG" IS ACTUALLY A DRY-ROASTED PEANUT.

CRUNCH CRUNCH CRUNCH

I DON'T KNOW... DO YOU GUYS LIKE IT? IT'S A LITTLE..."POOFY."

I LIKE MOHAIR.

I WANT SOMETHING THAT MAKES ME LOOK "RUGGED," YOU KNOW?

"RUGGED"? ROB, YOU WORK IN ADVERTISING!

YEAH. ON A MAKE-UP ACCOUNT.

HEY! I'M NAKED IN HERE! DO YOU MIND?!

SATCHEL, YOU'RE **ALWAYS** NAKED.

BUT THIS IS "BATHROOM NAKED"...

PICKY, PICKY...

ALL I'M ASKING IS FOR MY BOUNDARIES TO BE RESPECTED...

HEY THERE, SWEET CHEEKS.

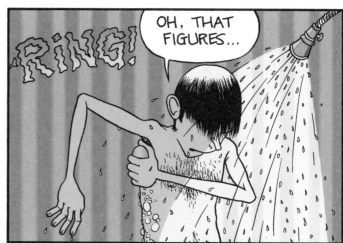

UH-OH... BUCKY'S BOOSTER SHOTS ARE DUE...

OH, DEAR.

HE BROKE TWO CAR DOORS LAST TIME.

DOES THE VET STILL MAKE HOUSE CALLS?

NOT TO THIS HOUSE, NO.

OH, RIIIIGHT. THE HOCKEY STICK INCIDENT, I FORGOT...

WELL, TODAY'S THE DAY... GOTTA GET BUCKY TO THE VET.

OH, THIS IS BAD. **BAD.**

DO YOU THINK HE'LL NOTICE IF I'M WEARING HOCKEY GLOVES AS WE GET NEAR THE CAR?

NNNO! HE'S NOT THAT OBSERVANT, IS HE?

WHAT'S GOING ON IN HERE? I SMELL FEAR...

WHAT'S THE KIDDIE SEAT FOR?

ARE YOU PREGNANT?!

CUT IT OUT, SATCHEL, IT'S TO STRAP BUCKY IN SO WE CAN GO TO THE VET.

OH...WELL WHAT'S THE PIÑATA FOR?

THAT'S THE DECOY SO I HAVE AN EXCUSE TO GET A BLINDFOLD ON HIM FIRST.

EFFORTS TO SECURE BUCKY INTO THE KIDDIE SEAT PROVE FUTILE. PLAN "B" IS ENACTED...

OOH! SOMEONE'S LEFT A NICE, BIG LOLLIPOP ON THE SPECIAL CHAIR!

I KNOW WHAT YOU'RE TRYING TO-

NOW!

HEY!

OOF!

WELL *THIS* DOESN'T SEEM RIGHT...

IT'LL DO.

OK, BUCKY, LET'S HAVE A LOOK AT YOUR TEETH...

WHEW! MR. WILCO, DON'T YOU **EVER** CLEAN HIS TEETH?

DO I LOOK INSANE?

WELL, YOU COULD HAVE SCOOPED OUT THESE CHUNKS OF TUNA FOR MY SAKE.

YEAH, I TRIED THAT IN THE WAITING ROOM... YOU'RE OUT OF GAUZE NOW, BY THE WAY.

I HOPE I'M NOT UNDERDRESSED FOR MY DATE...

NAH, SHE LOOKS PRETTY CASUAL...

HOW DO YOU KNOW WHAT SHE LOOKS LIKE?

WELL...SHE'S IN THE LIVING ROOM. ...WITH BUCKY... I THOUGHT YOU KNEW.

...WHAT?

SO...YOU'RE CLASSIER THAN MOST OF THE TRASH ROB DATES...

by darby conley

WHATCHA DOIN'?

MAKING A BOOKCASE!

I GUESS IT'S A GOOD THING HE DOESN'T ACTUALLY HAVE ANY BOOKS TO GO ON THAT...

A FEW "HOW TO" BOOKS WOULDN'T HURT...

HEY!

I TOLD YOU NOT TO SQUIRT WHIPPED-CREAM INTO YOUR MOUTH!!

SQQQQT!

I'M A **CAT**... I'M FOLLOWING MY INSTINCTS. IT'S MY "CHARM".

ARE THESE THE SAME "INSTINCTS" THAT MADE YOU BITE ME THIS MORNING?

THAT WOULD BE "YES".

THEN YOU, AND YOUR "CHARM," ARE GROUNDED.

ISN'T THIS A NEW COUCH? IT'S ALL SHREDDED.

YEAH, BUCKY DOES THAT.

HE'S "SIAMESE," RIGHT?

WELL, CROSSED WITH SOMETHING ELSE, YEAH.

CROSSED WITH WHAT?

I DUNNO... A CHAIN SAW, MAYBE.

SO A BUNCH OF STUPID "MARKET RESEARCH" CAME IN AND NOW I HAVE TO REDO AN ENTIRE ACCOUNT TONIGHT.

CAN I SEE?

HMM. WELL, ACTUALLY, I'M INCLINED TO AGREE WITH THIS ANALYSIS. THE PRESENT AD CAMPAIGN MAY ELICIT UNINTENDED NEGATIVE IMAGES, AT LEAST ON AN UNCONSCIOUS LEVEL... ROB? YOU OK?

WHAT? OH, SORRY, I'M HAVING A HARD TIME LISTENING TO YOU WHILE YOU'RE HOLDING MR. BONES.

LIFE WITH THE FLU...

Click!

LIFE WITH THE FLU CONTINUES...

Snotti Tissues

TV LIST

NACHO SHARDS

HEY. WHAT ARE YOU DOING?

TAKING SATCHEL'S TEMPERATURE.

I KNOW IT'S NOT AN "ORAL" THERMOMETER, BUT WHY IS IT IN HIS *EAR*?

IT'S **FOR** EARS... WHY? WHERE DID YOU... OH, NO...

WOOPS.

WHAT ARE YOU GUYS TALKING ABOUT? I CAN'T HEAR YOU...

by darby conley

SO LET'S SEE THE NEW PET FISH YOU'RE SO PROUD OF.

I THINK THEY'RE STILL SETTLING INTO THE NEW TANK.

EEW! SATCHEL, THESE ARE SARDINES!

YOUR POINT BEING...

THEY'RE NOT "PETS," THEY'RE FOOD! THEY'RE NOT EVEN ALIVE!

THEN WHY DOES IT TELL YOU HOW TO PREPARE THEIR WATER ON THE CAN?

"PETS" DON'T COME IN "CANS." SATCHEL...

THIS IS A RECIPE FOR FISH CHOWDER.

OH...I THOUGHT IT CALLED FOR A LOT OF BUTTER.

28

HI! IS THIS YOUR KITTY? I'M MOVING IN NEXT DOOR AND HE WAS UNDER MY SOFA IN THE HALL.

UMM...YES. BUCKY IS MINE...HIS NAME IS "BUCKY"...**HI.**

MY NAME IS LAURA. HE'S CUTE.

I'M BUCKY... I MEAN *"ROB".* THANKS...FOR SAYING I'M CUTE – I MEAN *BUCKY* IS.

SHE IS **SO** CUTE.

BUCKY IS **SO** CUTE.

O·HO! SO NOW THAT YOU'RE ALL SLEEPY AND WANT A WARM LAP, YOU'LL BE SOCIAL, EH?

EDITOR'S NOTE:

A PORTION OF THIS CARTOON HAS BEEN CENSORED DUE TO ITS VIOLENT CONTENT.

WHY DO YOU PROVOKE HIM LIKE THAT?

EAT THAT! I'M NOT MAKING YOU ANYTHING ELSE! *EAT IT!*

POOR BUCKY, YELLED AT ALL THE TIME... MAYBE HE DOESN'T **LIKE** THAT CAT FOOD.

IT'S $3-A-CAN GREEK TUNA. IT'S THE ONLY ☆@#% THING HE'LL EAT – *THAT'S ACTUALLY "FOOD"* – AND HE **STILL** LETS IT **ROT.**

NOW HE'S CHEWING ON YOUR CASHMERE SCARF...

OHH, POOR KITTY MUST BE *STARVING!* WELL... IF YOU NEED TO EAT THAT –

I'M NOT HUNGRY.

SO...YOU'RE TELLIN' ME THAT YOU HAVE "NO IDEA" WHY THE MEAT LOAF IS ON THE FLOOR HALF-EATEN.

IT'S A MYSTERY... I'M JUST AS SHOCKED AS YOU.

FUNNY, THOUGH, HOW MANY OF THESE "MYSTERIES" HAVE KITTY PAW PRINTS ALL OVER THEM.

YEAH... SURE IS FREAKY...

EVERYONE LAUGHED AT ME WHEN I BOUGHT THIS JUMBO BOTTLE OF IBUPROFEN... WELL

HA!

"WE'LL NEVER USE THEM UP BEFORE THE EXPIRATION DATE," YOU SAID! "IT'S WASTEFUL," YOU SAID! WELL HA TO YOU! IT'S STILL TWO WEEKS TILL THEY EXPIRE, THERE'S ONLY 12 PILLS LEFT, AND I JUST GOT SICK!! HA, HA, HA! cough! cough!

I WISH HE'D JUST GO LIE DOWN...

HOPE THAT STUFF LOWERS HIS FEVER.

CAN YOU OPEN THIS CAP FOR ME?

WHERE ARE YOU GOING? IT'S MIDNIGHT...

I WANT TO CHECK ON A PRINTING AT THE NEWSPAPER.

CAN I COME?

NO, LAST TIME YOU CAME TO A PRESS CHECK, YOU DISAPPEARED FOR AN HOUR, AND THE NEXT DAY 650,000 COPIES OF THE "BOSTON GLOB" GOT SENT ALL OVER NEW ENGLAND.

WAS THAT WORSE THAN THE "NEW YORK PEST" INCIDENT?

NO. JUST MORE RECENT.

MANNN, YOU DON'T LET ME DO ANYTHING.

34

I HAVE NO IDEA WHO WOULD BE A GOOD SPOKESPERSON FOR "SPARKY TOOLS".

WE DON'T HAVE MUCH IN THE BUDGET, EITHER...

THEY'VE GOTTA BE FUNNY, YET SERIOUS; "HARMLESS," YET WITH A LITTLE BIT OF "BAD BOY" IN 'EM.

YEAH. THE "BAD BOY" THING IS KEY.

MR. WILCO, YOUR CAT SAYS HE'S LOOKING FOR YOU, BUT WE KEEP FINDING HIM IN THE LADIES' ROOM.

NO, TODD, I DON'T WANT MY **CAT** TO BE THE SPOKESMAN FOR A POWER TOOL COMPANY.

ROBBIE-BABY. BE REASONABLE... HE'S CUTE, HE'S TOUGH, HE'S EXACTLY WHAT WE'RE LOOKING FOR.

WE'VE BEEN LOOKING FOR A LUMBERJACK...

LOOK, ROB, WE'RE OVER BUDGET... HE'S A **CAT**. HE'S **YOUR** CAT. AND I **LIKE** HIM. WE CAN PAY HIM IN TUNA, AND IF YOU DON'T LIKE IT, I CAN ALWAYS PUT YOU BACK ON THE "KISSY LIPS" ADS.

YOU MAKE A PERSUASIVE ARGUMENT. HE LIKES HIS TUNA IN OIL.

ROB, I DON'T SEE HOW YOU CAN OBJECT TO THIS FACE SELLING POWER TOOLS - THE EYES, THE CLAWS... THE *FANG!* IN FACT, WE'LL CALL HIM "FANG THE TOOL CAT"!

HIS NAME IS "BUCKY".

"BUCKY" - SURE, THAT WORKS TOO. "BUCKY THE TOOL CAT."

NO, I LIKE "FANG".

OH, SINCE WHEN DO YOU RESPOND TO *ANY* NAME?!

BUCKY SAYS HE'S GONNA BE IN A TV AD...

NOT IF I CAN HELP IT.

HE'S BEEN SHOWING ME ALL THE FREEBIES HE GOT FROM THE TOOL COMPANY.

WHAT "FREEBIES"?

YRRR!

BUCKY, I DECIDED THAT YOU CAN'T DO THE ADS FOR "SPARKY TOOLS." WE'LL HAVE TO RETURN THESE FREE TOOLS.

AW, MANNN.

EEW! THIS SANDER IS COVERED IN... WHAT IS THIS, MEAT?!

THE HAM WAS FATTY... I TRIMMED IT.

?

YOU EVER WONDER WHAT HE CARRIES AROUND IN THAT BACKPACK?

UMMM... NNNO...

DID MS. PRETTY LIKE OUR TRIP TO THE YARD? WOULD MS. PRETTY LIKE SOME TEA NOW?

CAN'T WE **EVER** WATCH SOMETHING OTHER THAN THE ANIMAL CHANNEL?

EVERYONE WHO WANTS TO WATCH THE ANIMAL CHANNEL RAISE YOUR HAND... SORRY, ROB... 2 TO 1...

SORRY, SATCHEL...BUCKY DOESN'T *MEAN* TO BE SUCH A PEST WHEN HE CHASES YOU AROUND...HE'S A **CAT**...HE CAN'T CONTROL HIS "MIDNIGHT CRAZIES."

BUT I BUMPED MY NOSE AND STUBBED MY TOE... **AND** KNOCKED OVER 2 PLANTS...WHY DOES HE CHASE **ME**?

WHO KNOWS?...:"WHY DID THE CHICKEN CROSS THE ROAD?"

"CHICKEN"? WHAT "CHICKEN"? DID BUCKY CHASE IT TOO? CAN I TALK TO THIS CHICKEN?

LOOK! THERE'S A McDOODLES.

NO, BUCKY.

I WANT A HOWDY MEAL. I'M HUNGRY.

WE ARE **NOT** GOING TO McDOODLES. I'M TIRED AND I WANT TO GO HOME.

I WANT A HOWDY MEAL! WITH A **TOY**!!

ACTUALLY, I WOULDN'T MIND A BIG SLOPPER...

NO! **NO!** YOU GUYS ARE **SO** IMMATURE! I WANNA GO HOME! *I WANNA GO HOME!!*

38

HEY, ROBBO, HOW CAN YOU TELL THE DIFFERENCE BETWEEN THE MAYOR AND A SCRATCHING POST?

OH, THAT'S A GOOD ONE... THIS IS FUN... HMM...

NO, SERIOUSLY, HOW CAN YOU TELL? IT MAY BE "IMPORTANT."

OK, I DON'T LIKE THIS RIDDLE ANYMORE.

HEY, THERE'S A POLICE CAR OUTSIDE...

OK, I'M GOING TO GET SOME CASH. YOU WAIT HERE. OH, LOOK, GO TALK TO THAT DOG OVER THERE, SHE'S CUTE.

FIRST MERG BANK

PUSH

UMM, HEY...

MY GUY IS IN THE —

YOU SMELL FUNNY.

HEY! SLOW DOWN!

SNORT!

SLOP!

MUNCH!

GULP!

I GUESS IF YOU SLEEP 20 HOURS A DAY, YOU HAVE TO WORK PRETTY FAST WHEN YOU **ARE** AWAKE...

NNNNNN!

WHERE'S THE TV REMOTE?!

I LIKE IT BETTER WHEN HE'S ASLEEP.

WHAT'S WRONG WITH YOUR GLASSES?

THEY'RE NEW "OLIVE PEEPERS" DESIGNER GLASSES. LIKE 'EM?

UM...WELL, THEY DON'T SEEM QUITE "RIGHT"...

TELL IT LIKE IT IS, HOMEY.

BE QUIET, BUCKY— WHAT DO YOU MEAN BY THAT, SATCHEL?

WELL...I MEAN THEY LOOK SORT OF..."ODD."

ATTA BOY, SATCHEL! HIT 'IM WHERE IT HURTS!

SHUT UP, BUCKY— WHAT DO YOU MEAN "ODD"?!

THEY JUST MIGHT NOT "SUIT" YOU ENTIRELY...

AWW, WHAT DOES A DOG KNOW?

THERE YOU GO, ROBBO! GIVE 'IM A DOSE OF HIS OWN MEDICINE!

darb

YOUR TURN, SATCHEL! STICK IT TO THE MAN!

NOW, YOUR NEW SHIRT I LIKE.

YEAH, IT'S GOOD.

44

I'M THANKFUL THAT SATCHEL TOOK A BATH AND ISN'T STINKING UP THE HOUSE...

TRY AGAIN.

I'M THANKFUL YOU DIDN'T BURN THE TURKEY BEYOND **ALL** RECOGNITION THIS YEAR...

BUCKY, WE'RE JUST GOING TO SIT HERE UNTIL YOU TAKE THIS SERIOUSLY. YOU MIGHT AS WELL JUST DO IT RIGHT.

I THINK SOME WEIRD...LIKE... *TRASH* FELL INTO MY BOWL.

IT'S "NÜTRØKKÄT" DIET CAT FOOD. EAT IT....IT'S SWEDISH.

BUCKY

BUT I'M A **SIAMESE.**

THAT NEVER STOPS YOU FROM EATING "FRENCH FRIES"...EAT IT.

I'M NOT GOING TO EAT THIS DIET FOOD... I DON'T CARE IF IT'S "SWEDISH."

WE'RE ALL ON SPECIAL EUROPEAN DIETS, BUCKY.

I WANT WHAT SATCHEL'S EATING!

SURE, I'LL TRADE, SWEDISH CAT FOOD SOUNDS BETTER THAN "CZECH CHOW."

JUST EAT YOUR OWN FOOD... YOU'LL LIKE IT.

WELL... I'LL TRY IT. BUT YOU CAN JUST CHECK THE HALL CARPET IN TEN MINUTES TO SEE HOW MUCH I "LIKED" IT...

WHOA!

BUCKY, YOUR STUPID BALL IS IN THE MIDDLE OF THE FLOOR — AND *HEY!* IT'S PAINTED TO MATCH THE CARPET!

THAT'S CRAZY TALK.

YOU KNOW... SOME PEOPLE THINK THAT CATS ARE "EVIL."

THAT'S FUNNY, SOME CATS THINK THAT PEOPLE HAVE ENOUGH SENSE TO LOOK WHERE THEY'RE GOING.

OOO! BEEF JERKY! GIVE ME ONE!

IF YOU COULD EVER ASK **NICELY** FOR A CHANGE, I MIGHT...

YOU MEAN.... STUFF I "SAY" DIRECTLY AFFECTS STUFF I "GET"?

OF COURSE IT DOES!

I **LOVE YOU,** ROB...

HMMM.

MAKE HIM LOOK YOU IN THE EYE AND SAY THAT.

AW, JEEZ, FOR ONCE COULD YOU NOT PUT YOUR FOOD ON THE CARPET?! THE LEAST YOU COULD DO IS USE THE WOOD FLOOR!

WELL, YOU PUT ALL **YOUR** FOOD ON CLEAN "DISH" THINGIES, THEN YOU GOTTA WASH THEM AGAIN-AT LEAST THE FLOOR IS **ALREADY** DIRTY.

OH, GOOD "LOGIC," BUCKY; IT ALL MAKES SENSE NOW. THANK YOU FOR ENLIGHTENING ME...

YOU'RE WELCOME.

SO YOU THINK HE ACTUALLY SAW A GHOST?

WELL... WHAT ELSE COULD POSSIBLY— *OH!*

THERE! IN THE CORNER!

DEAR GOD!

A "MOUSE"?

MY CAT IS TERRIFIED OF MICE?!

DON'T YOU HAVE ANYTHING TO SAY FOR YOURSELF AFTER LAST NIGHT, BUCKY?...THAT TINY MOUSE SCARED YOU *NUMB.*

YOU WERE DROOLING EVERYWHERE.

WELL?

I HAVE NO RECOLLECTION OF THE EVENTS OF LAST NIGHT.

I SUPPOSE THAT'S JUST AS WELL... YOU CAME OFF LOOKIN' PRETTY BAD.

WE'RE LOOKING FOR A CHRISTMAS PRESENT FOR OUR GUY...

MAY I SUGGEST THE LATEST IN EUROPEAN GROOMING...

THE KLAUSKUTTEN® ELECTRIC RAZOR HAS 5 SELF-SHARPENING BLADES WHICH ROTATE INDEPENDENTLY AT A PRECISE 60 CYCLES PER SECOND. IT LIFTS AND CUTS EACH HAIR IN 3 STAGES. AND ITS PATENTED SIDEBURN TRIMMER HAS 8 VARIABLE HEIGHT SETTINGS. IT IS THE ULTIMATE SHAVING EXPERIENCE.

HMM.

CAN IT SCALE A FISH?

...WE DON'T RECOMMEND THAT, SIR.

ROB...ROB... **ROB!** WAKE UP!

HNNNn....WHUM? WHAYA WANT, BUCKY?

I WANT TO GO OUT.

SO, USE THE *CAT FLAP!* THAT'S WHY I PUT IT IN, YOU DUMB CAT!

I LIKE THE WAY WE USED TO DO IT...

YOU MEAN, YOU *LIKE* WAKING ME UP?!

I GUESS I JUST LIKE BEING "SEEN."

TELL YA WHAT - I'LL WATCH YOU GET OUT OF MY ROOM.

56

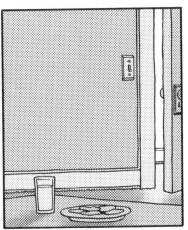

BUCKY, HAVE YOU SEEN THE REMOTE?

WELL, ROB, LEMME TELL YA - I DON'T SEE TOO MUCH OF ANYTHING WHILE I'M IN THE "ZONE."

WHAT?! "IN THE ZONE"? YOU FEELIN' OK?

YEAH, AFTER I SETTLED DOWN, I FELT PRETTY GOOD. THIS ONE WAS REALLY SPECIAL.

WHERE THE HECK DID YOU LEARN SPORTS CLICHÉS? STOP IT!

NO, NO, I HAVE TO GIVE 110%. ...ONE DAY AT A TIME.

I DON'T THINK YOU TWO ARE ON THE SAME PAGE...

BUCKY, DID YOU USE THE TUB WITHOUT CLEANING IT OUT? IT'S ALL NASTY...

DON'T LOOK AT ME... I HAVEN'T TAKEN A BATH SINCE MAY '96.

...THAT'S NOT EXACTLY WHAT I WANTED TO HEAR, BUCKY...

OK, THEN, "NO," I DID NOT USE IT. GO ASK "SMELLY-THE-DOG."

IT SAYS HERE THAT ONE OUT OF FIFTY PEOPLE HEARS VOICES IN HIS HEAD...

I HEAR VOICES IN MY HEAD CONSTANTLY..."DON'T TEAR UP THE COUCH," OR "DON'T JUMP ON ME WHILE I'M SLEEPING," OR "STOP BITING ME"...IT'S ANNOYING.

SLURP

BUCKY...THAT'S ME TELLING Y—

I NEVER LISTEN TO THEM, THOUGH.

60

61

YOU SEE, WHEN YOU BITE SATCHEL'S **ARM**, YOU HURT HIS **FEELINGS**, TOO... I THINK IT WOULD BE NICE IF YOU TOLD HIM YOU WERE SORRY.

BUCKY, WE'RE WAITING F—

YOU GUYS ARE LIKE THE BIGGEST FRUITCAKES. SERIOUSLY, IT'S EMBARRASSING.

THAT BURRITO MADE ME SICK...

WHAT "BURRITO"?

IN THE FRIDGE... IN A DELI BAG... IT WAS **HUGE.**

THAT WASN'T A "BURRITO"; IT WAS A MEATBALL SUB WRAPPED IN PAPER! AND IF THE *TAPE* DIDN'T TIP YOU OFF, THE *LAYER OF TINFOIL SHOULD HAVE!*

OH... WELL, IT **TASTED** GOOD...

DOGS ARE SO STUPID.

MAN, HOW CAN YOU WATCH THIS SHOW?! IT'S TERRIBLE!

DON'T LOOK AT ME—THIS IS BUCKY'S PROGRAM!

OHH NO! YOU CAN'T BLAME **EVERYTHING** ON ME! I THOUGHT THIS WAS **YOUR** CRUDDY SHOW!

IN MY DEFENSE, YOUR FRIEND'S ROCK GARDEN LOOKED LIKE A LITTER BOX...

I'M NOT TALKING TO YOU.

HE'S CUTE.

...EXCUSE ME?

YOUR CAT... HE'S "CUTE"...

MY CAT?

UMM...YEAH... ...LOOK, I'M SORRY IF—

you want him?

I **HEARD** THAT!

MY PIE LOOKS FUNNY. DID IT FALL ON THE FLOOR?

Y- UMM... *NNNO...*

BUT IT'S BROKEN... AND IT'S GOT STUFF ALL OVER IT...

NAHH, THOSE ARE JUST "GARNISHES"...YOU KNOW, "FANCY", LIKE MARTHA STEWART DOES IT...

I'M A "*DOG*", I'M NOT "**STUPID**"! MARTHA STEWART DOESN'T GARNISH WITH **CAT HAIRS**! I'M GONNA EAT IT, JUST TELL ME WHAT'S WRONG WITH IT!

OK, I **DROPPED** IT! I'M SORRY I'M NOT PERFECT LIKE YOU "*DOGS*"!

ROB, BUCKY BIT ME AND HE WON'T APOLOGIZE!

I *DID NOT!* AND HE CALLED ME A *FELINE!*

HE *IS* A FELINE!

BUCKY, "FELINE" JUST MEANS—

DON'T *YOU* START!

I CAN **SEE** THAT YOU BIT HIM; I'M *TRYING* TO GIVE YOU A CHANCE TO DO THE RIGHT THING.

WELL, IT, UM... I... *HE BIT ME FIRST!* ON MY *EAR!*

OH, THAT IS **SO** UNTRUE!

YOUR EARS LOOK FINE.

HUH? OH...YEAH. I MEANT TO SAY MY *ARM.* ...UNDER MY FUR... YOU CAN'T SEE IT. IT HURTS, THOUGH. ..."OW."

SO YOU, LIKE, "FORGOT" WHERE HE BIT YOU FOR A MINUTE?

YEAH... I MUST BE "IN SHOCK."

OK, NOW I **KNOW** YOU'RE LYING. GO TO YOUR CLOSET.

DANG.

HEY, BUCKY, WHAT'S UP?

LOOK AT YOURSELF, MAN... SHAG CARPET... BEAN BAG... "BENJI" POSTERS... YOU'RE LIVIN' IN THE **PAST**...

I LIKE LIVING IN THE PAST... IT'S SO PREDICTABLE...

I LOVE CATNIP MICE... IT'S WHY I CHEW THEIR HEADS OFF. THEY'RE GOOD FOR BREAKFAST.

1, 2, 3, 4, 5...

THAT WAS A **HAIKU**... A FREAKY, LITTLE *CAT* HAIKU...

ROB, CAN I HAVE A LOAN? I WANT A NEW HEATING PAD.

GEE, I DUNNO, BUCKY... DO YOU HAVE ANY "COLLATERAL"? ...SOMETHING TO SHOW ME YOU DESERVE MY MONEY?...

I HAVE A **HUGE** FANG...

THAT'S NOT "COLLATERAL". BUCKY, THAT'S JUST A THREAT.

BUCKY, YOU'RE GONNA TRY THE VEGGIE LOAF, AND THAT'S **THAT.** YOU CAN'T GO AROUND EATING ALL MY PLANTS AND THEN CLAIM THAT YOU DON'T EAT VEGETABLES...

"*TECHNICALLY,*" I DON'T THINK I REALLY "EAT" PLANTS IF ALL I'M DOING IS CHEWING THEM UP AND SPITTING THEM OUT.

WELL, NOW... SEE, THAT'S A WHOLE **DIFFERENT** PROBLEM.

I WANTED TUNA, BUT **NO!** YOU MADE *VEGGIE LOAF!* WELL, YOU SHOULDN'T HAVE LEFT IT ON THE TABLE, 'CAUSE **I ATE IT!** IT WAS **DISGUSTING,** BUT JUST SO **YOU** COULDN'T HAVE IT, I ATE THE **WHOLE THING** — PARSLEY AND ALL, BABY!

ARE YA FINISHED?

...YEAH...

THE VEGGIE LOAF IS IN THE OVEN. **YOU** ATE THE LIMA BEAN SATCHEL PLANTED LAST WEEK... **DIRT AND ALL, BABY!**

AWWW, BUCKY! IT **JUST** SPROUTED!

HMM. YEAH, THAT MAKES SENSE, ACTUALLY.

SATCHEL, HAVE I EVER TOLD YOU HOW WONDERFUL A DOG YOU ARE?

I ATE MY BEEF JERKY ALREADY, BUCKY.

NUTS.

73

HI, GUYS! HEY, ROB, HOW'S THAT VIOLET I GAVE YOU DOING?

HI, LAURA, GEE, I'M SORRY ABOUT THAT - BUCKY ALREADY ATE IT... HE DESTROYS ALL MY PLANTS.

HAVE YOU TRIED PUTTING CAYENNE PEPPER ON THEM?

YEAHHH, IT DIDN'T WORK.

HE LIKES SPICY FOOD.

I'M GOING OUT WITH KATE TONIGHT, SO SATCHEL IS IN CHARGE WHILE I'M GONE.

SATCHEL WAS IN CHARGE LAST TIME... IT'S MY TURN.

JUST HOW DUMB DO YOU THINK I AM?

WELL... I GUESS YOU AREN'T AS DUMB AS I HOPED...

GEE, HOW FLATTERING.

... BUT THERE'S NO **WAY** YOU COULD BE AS DUMB AS YOU *LOOK*.

WHATEVER HAPPENED TO THAT "KELLIE" WOMAN? AREN'T YOU TWO A "THING"?

WE HAD ONE DATE, 6 MONTHS AGO, SATCHEL.

SHE DUMPED YOU, EH?

ACTUALLY, HER FRIEND TOLD ME THAT SHE WAS FREAKED OUT THAT MY PETS STOWED AWAY IN THE TRUNK OF MY CAR DURING THE DATE AND CHEWED THE STRAP OFF HER PURSE.

SHE'S OBVIOUSLY LYING TO PROTECT YOUR FEELINGS.

MY DATE WENT *GREAT!* IT WENT SO WELL I MIGHT SEND HER FLOWERS TOMORROW.

COOL! AND YOU CAN MAKE THE CARD WITH THE MESSAGE ON IT *GREEN!*

WHY?

BUCKY SAID THAT SINCE SHE WENT OUT WITH YOU, SHE MUST NEED A "GREEN CARD."

HEY!

WHAT? I DON'T EVEN KNOW WHAT THAT MEANS!

SO YOU HAD A GOOD TIME ON YOUR DATE LAST NIGHT, EH?

YES, I DID HAVE A GOOD TIME. AND BY THE WAY, **NO**, SHE DOESN'T NEED A *GREEN CARD.*

IS SHE GONNA COME HERE? I WANT TO TEST... I MEAN, **MEET**, HER...

WELL, IF SHE DOES COME OVER, YOU BE *NICE* TO HER. SHE REALLY WANTS TO MEET YOU. SHE LOVES CATS.

SHE **DOES**? OH... NEVER MIND, SOMEHOW I'VE LOST INTEREST.

YO, ROBBO, WHAT DO YOU THINK I SHOULD BE WHEN I GROW UP?

WHAT DO YOU MEAN?

WHEN I GROW UP...LIKE YOU...I FIGURE I'LL GET ONE OF THOSE "JOB" THINGIES. I GUESS I'LL BE A ROCK STAR.

BUCKY, YOU ARE GROWN UP...YOU'RE A FULLY-GROWN CAT.

THIS IS AS BIG AS I'M GONNA GET? YOU'RE, LIKE, 12 FEET HIGH!

OHHH, GO TAKE A NAP.

WHAT'S A... "PARALEGAL"?

I DUNNO...I WOULDN'T THINK YOU COULD DO IT, THOUGH.

HOW DO YOU KNOW I CAN'T DO IT?

I WOULD IMAGINE THAT IF YOU CAN'T **PRONOUNCE** A JOB, YOU CAN'T **DO** THE JOB...

WELL...YOU DON'T KNOW THAT...AT LEAST I *LIKE* THAT WORD - A TON OF THESE SAY "9 TO 5"... NOW, I'M NO LAZY *LAPCAT*, BUT THAT'S **OFFENSIVE**.

DO YOU WANT TO READ THE MANUSCRIPT I WROTE? IT'S SORT OF, LIKE, MY REFLECTIONS ON BEING A CAT.

HMM...WELL, BESIDES THE FACT THAT YOU'RE THE WORST SPELLER I'VE EVER SEEN, I JUST DON'T KNOW IF PEOPLE WILL WANT TO READ 185 PAGES ABOUT STARING AT A WALL...THERE'S NO *PLOT*...

I WRITE WHAT I KNOW.

I MEAN, *"CHAPTER 24: IN WHICH I SHIFT MY BUTT..."* I DON'T WANNA READ THAT.

I'VE BEEN THINKIN' THAT INSTEAD OF A "JOB", I SHOULD SET UP A *WEB SITE*.

WHAT FOR?

WELL... I COULD POST MY VIEWS ON CONTROVERSIAL ISSUES, GIVE STOCK TIPS...AND I COULD HAVE PEOPLE SEND ME MONEY.

IF IT GAVE ADVICE ON TREATING SCRATCHES, I'D USE IT.

IT COULD BE: WWW.WACKEDOUTPET.COM.

OOOO, DO YOU THINK THAT'S STILL AVAILABLE?

SO WHY DIDN'T YOU LIKE MY BOOK?

IT'S NOT "BAD"; YOU JUST NEED TO HAVE SOMETHING TO TALK ABOUT, LIKE A PERSONAL TRAGEDY OR TRIUMPH...

"TRAGEDY OR TRIUMPH"? JEEZ, YOU REALLY DON'T LET ME OUT THAT MUCH...

WHAT IF SOMETHING TRAGIC HAPPENED TO **SATCHEL**, COULD I WRITE ABOUT THAT?

NO.

CAN YOU MAIL THIS FOR ME? I'M SENDING MY MANUSCRIPT TO A PUBLISHER.

SURE... WHY IS IT SO LUMPY?

I FIGURED IT WOULDN'T HURT TO BUTTER THE EDITOR UP WITH A GIFT.

I DON'T WANT TO KNOW WHAT IT IS, DO I?

WHY NOT? **OH,** NO, DON'T WORRY, IT'S ALREADY DEAD.

IF YOU SAY THAT ONE MORE TIME, I'LL-- **STOP SAYING THAT!** ARE YOU LISTENING TO ME?! HEY!. BE **QUIET!**

YOU'D BETTER DO SOMETHING ABOUT BUCKY; HE'S YELLING AT SOMEONE ON THE PHONE.

SERIOUSLY? HA HA HA!!

WHY ARE YOU LAUGHING? HE'S REALLY SCREAMING AT SOMEBODY.

NO, NO - HE MADE ME CALL A PUBLISHER ABOUT HIS "BOOK," AND THEN YANKED THE PHONE AWAY FROM ME AND STARTED YELLING AT A RECORDED MESSAGE... HE STARTED AN **HOUR** AGO!

WHATCHA DOIN'?

SUSIE AT WORK'S BIRTHDAY IS COMING UP AND IT'S MY TURN TO FIGURE OUT WHAT TO DO...

WE COULD WAIT ON THE TOP SHELF OF HER CLOSET ALL NIGHT AND, WHEN SHE OPENS IT IN THE MORNING, WE COULD ALL JUMP ON HER HEAD SCREAMING.

WE'LL CALL THAT "PLAN B"...

"B" FOR BUCKY!

COOL.

PSST! CAN YOU KEEP IT DOWN WHILE I'M ON THE PHONE?

SORRY, I'M ON THE PHONE, TOO, BUT WE HAVE A BAD CONNECTION, SO I HAVE TO YELL.

SATCH, YOU'RE YELLING INTO THE TV REMOTE.

THEN......WHO WAS I TALKING TO?

ROB?...HI! LONG TIME NO SEE!

HI, JANICE, YEAH, IT'S BEEN A WHILE.

OH, AND HERE'S LITTLE BUCKY. HE'S SO CUTE IN HIS LITTLE CARRIER--NOW BE HONEST, ROB, YOU JUST CARRY HIM AROUND TO MEET WOMEN, DON'T YOU?

YOUR HAIR USED TO BE ALL DARK...NOW IT FADES FROM BLACK TO WHITE......LIKE A GERMAN SHEPHERD. I DON'T LIKE IT.

I DON'T MEET MANY WOMEN THIS WAY.

82

MAN, THAT WAS *TOTALLY* HUMILIATING... IF I HAD KNOWN THAT ALARM WAS JUST A *DRILL*, I'D AT LEAST HAVE GRABBED A *SHIRT* BEFORE RUNNING OUTSIDE IN MY *UNDERWEAR*...

I DON'T SEE WHAT THE BIG DEAL IS... I DON'T HAVE A SHIRT ON.

BUCKY, YOU'RE *USED* TO BEING NAKED IN PUBLIC - YOU'RE *ALWAYS* NAKED - YOU DON'T CARE...

WOW, THAT MAKES ME SOUND *SO* COOL...

BUT *WHY* CAN'T I VOTE?

WELL...YOU'RE A DOG...ONLY PEOPLE CAN VOTE...

I THOUGHT DOGS WERE JUST DIFFERENT *KINDS* OF PEOPLE... LIKE "FRENCH" PEOPLE...

DO YOU REMEMBER THAT TIME YOU ASKED ME WHY *PANTS* NEVER FIT YOU?

YEAH...

THIS IS SO SAD...

HEY! MY CAR'S HOOD ORNAMENT! YOU TOLD ME YOU LOST THAT!

WHAT, THIS? NO, NO, THIS IS MY...UM... *ASTROLOGICAL* SIGN...

OHHH, I DIDN'T REALIZE YOU WERE A *VOLKSWAGON* - NOW HAND IT OVER, YOU LOOK LIKE A *FOOL*.

...AND YET I *FEEL* LIKE A TOTAL *STUD*.

THE FIRST PRINCIPLE OF
PAID ADVERTISING:

FATIGUE CLOUDS JUDGMENT

From the Rejected Character File:

#2: Flipper Brown, the Dung-Throwing Monkey

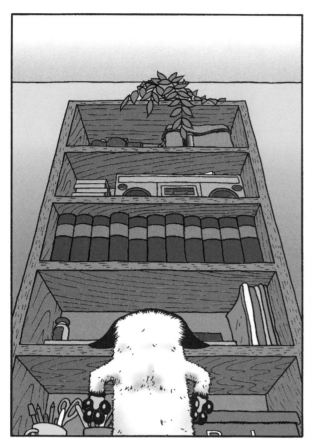

OH...ROB...*HI*...HOW LONG HAVE YOU—

LONG ENOUGH.

DOES YOUR SUDDEN INVOLVEMENT IN THIS "CAT-TIVIST" GROUP HAVE ANYTHING TO DO WITH SATCHEL JOINING HIS DOG CLUB? THE TIMING IS A LITTLE SUSPICIOUS...

HATE TO SAY IT, BUCK, BUT IT SORT OF MAKES YOU LOOK LIKE A "COPY CAT"...

NO, IT DOESN'T! ...AND WE PREFER THE TERM "FELICITOUS FELINE."

WELL, I DON'T KNOW IF I WANT YOU GOING TO THIS CAT RALLY — IT SOUNDS KINDA SKETCHY.

NO, NO, THERE'S A **LOT** OF US GOING — WE'RE MEETING UP WITH THE "LEGALIZE CATNIP" GROUP AND A RADICAL ANTI-DECLAWING GROUP.

AND WHAT ARE *THEY* CALLED? ...AS IF I COULDN'T GUESS...

"REBELS WITHOUT THE CLAWS."

WAIT... I THOUGHT CATNIP *WAS* LEGAL...

DON'T TRY TO FOLLOW ME — I'M NOT EVEN ALLOWED TO TELL YOU WHERE THE CAT RALLY IS.

OH, WHAT AM I GONNA DO? CALL ANIMAL CONTROL? STOP BEING SO MELODRAMATIC.

IF YOU'RE NOT WITH US, YOU'RE AGAINST US! OWNERS ARE ENEMIES OF THE MOVEMENT! *POWER TO THE CATS! WE WILL SCRATCH ALL THOSE WHO STAND IN OUR WAY!!!*

OK, *WHATEVER.* WATCH OUT FOR TRAFFIC.

SO I'M GOING TO THE RALLY... CAN I HAVE TWENTY BUCKS?

$20?! YOU'RE NOT ONLY A CAT, YOU'RE A *HIPPIE* CAT!

BUT, *ROB!* ACTIVISM COSTS MONEY! I NEED CAB FARE AND A *MEGAPHONE!*

HERE'S 85 CENTS - TAKE THE BUS AND SCREAM YOUR LUNGS OUT.

I GIVE IT HALF AN HOUR BEFORE THE CROWD FREAKS HIM OUT AND HE BITES SOMEBODY.

I DIDN'T EVEN THINK HE *LIKED* OTHER CATS.

HEYYY! THERE'S THE LITTLE ACTIVIST! HOW WAS THE RALLY?

NOT SO GOOD. WE GOT TO CITY HALL OK, BUT WHEN THE ALPHA CAT WENT TO SPEAK, HIS MEGAPHONE WAS SCREWING UP...

SO?

WELL... THE FEEDBACK FREAKED OUT ALL THE OTHER CATS... MOST OF US ENDED UP IN TRASH CANS OR UP TREES... I HID UNDER A CAR FOR TWO HOURS AND THEN I RAN HOME.

YOU DID THE RIGHT THING, BUCKY.

WELL, I'M SORRY TO HEAR THAT YOUR BIG PROTEST MARCH DIDN'T GO WELL. I COULD HAVE TOLD YOU THAT USING A SCREECHY MEGAPHONE ON A BUNCH OF WORKED-UP CATS WAS A RECIPE FOR DISASTER.

IT WASN'T A TOTAL LOSS... I GOT A T-SHIRT...

CHAT GUEVARA. CUTE.

WHAT DID YOU GUYS MAKE ME FOR DINNER? *OOO!* A CAN OF **TUNA!** AND IT'S ALREADY OPEN!

ONE THING I'LL GIVE BUCKY CREDIT FOR IS THAT HE'S NOT A FINICKY EATER.

MMMM.... HOLY **COW**, THIS IS GOOD! I HAVEN'T HAD TUNA SINCE... MAN, I DON'T **KNOW**... MUST BE SINCE, LIKE, **LUNCH** OR SOMETHING...

SATCHEL, THIS PACKAGE IS EMPTY. WAS IT ALL TORN UP LIKE THIS IN THE MAIL ROOM?

NO...

DON'T LOOK AT ME. I NEVER EVEN **SAW** THAT SWEATER.

WOW, HOW DID YOU KNOW IT WAS A SWEATER, BUCKY?

UMMM...

BUSTED.

WHOA, DUDE, IT'S *BOILING* IN HERE!

YEAH, SORRY, I HAVE TO KEEP IT THIS WAY BECAUSE OF BUCKY.

HE **LIKES** IT THIS HOT?

OH, NO, HE **HATES** IT, BUT IF HE EVER GETS COLD, HE TRIES TO CLIMB ON YOU TO GET WARM—AND THAT ALWAYS ENDS IN A "BAND-AID MOMENT."

EVERYBODY STAY AWAY FROM ME... I'M **HOT.**

WELL?

I BLAME THIS ON GRAVITY.

YEAH... THAT REALLY SEEMS TO BE AN ISSUE WITH YOU.

CLICK! CLICK! CLICK! CLICK! CLICK! CLICK! CLICK! CLICK! CLICK! CLICK! CLICK! CLICK!

sprouts

YOU CAN'T TURN ME OFF WITH THE REMOTE – NOW **GO CLEAN YOUR LITTERBOX!**

THEN... *MUTE! MUTE! MUTE! MUTE!*

CLICK! CLICK! CLICK! CLICK!

YOU'RE STILL COMIN' OVER TO WATCH THE GAME TONIGHT, RIGHT?

YEAH, TOTALLY. WHY?

I JUST NEED TO CALL HOME – IT'S GOOD TO ANNOUNCE VISITORS...

BECAUSE OF BUCKY?

YEAH... *WELL,* HIS *CLAWS,* SPECIFICALLY.

AND THE *FANG* – I'VE BEEN ON THE WRONG END OF THAT A FEW TIMES.

CAREFUL, JOE.

HEY THERE, TIGER, WHAT'S THE WORD ON THE STREET? WANT A LITTLE SCRITCH?

HEY! HE'S *PURRING!*... OR IS THAT THE SOUND HE MAKES RIGHT BEFORE HE — *OW!*

HE'S THE WEIRDEST LITTLE CREATURE I'VE EVER SEEN.

AND YET... I'M STRANGELY DRAWN TO HIM...

AW! HOLY COW! YOUR BLANKET IS **FOUL!** GO PUT THAT IN THE HAMPER, IT'S *FILTHY!*

IT'S NOT *"FILTHY"*- I HAVEN'T EVEN HAD IT FOR A *MONTH.* IT FELL OUT OF THE WINDOW AND I JUST FISHED IT OUT OF THE DUMPSTER...

JUST BECAUSE *YOU* DIDN'T GET IT DIRTY DOESN'T MEAN IT'S *"CLEAN"!* LOOK AT SATCHEL! IT'S MAKING HIM **DIZZY!**

OHHH, HE'S TOO SENSITIVE.

S N K K !

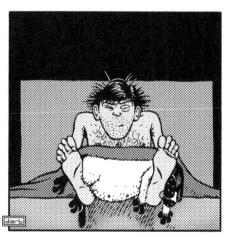

WHAT'S THAT?

IT'S ONE OF BUCKY'S ART PIECES FROM HIS BROKEN DISH COLLECTION. I GAVE HIM MY ALLOWANCE FOR IT...

SATCHEL! THAT'S JUST GONNA ENCOURAGE HIM TO BREAK MORE STUFF!

I DIDN'T WANT TO! HE SAID I DAMAGED IT WHEN I LOOKED AT IT!

"DAMAGED" IT?! HE...I...YOU... IT'S TRASH!

I GUESS I GOT CONFUSED! I'M SORRY! HE WAS BEING REALLY PUSHY!

BUCKY...WHY DID YOU WRITE YOUR NAME ON THE TOILET?

BY SIGNING MY NAME TO COMMON OBJECTS, THEY BECOME "ART". I CALL THESE OBJECTS "BUCKY-MADES."

YOU HAVE 15 MINUTES TO MAKE IT A "BUCKY-UNMADE."

SEE...WHEN YOU HAVE "VISION", EVEN THE UGLIEST THINGS CAN BE "ART."

YAWN... MORNING, GUYS. WHAT ARE WE TALKING ABOUT?

BUCKY, IT'S BAD ENOUGH THAT YOU'RE GOING AROUND BREAKING STUFF AND CALLING IT "ART," BUT SIGNING YOUR NAME ON SATCHEL IS TOTALLY UNACCEPTABLE...

DO YOU UNDERSTAND ME?! YOU'RE ON THIN ICE, KITTY!

MY ART DISTURBS YOU... THAT'S GOOD! USE THAT EMOTION!

KNOCK
KNOCK
KNOCK
KNOCK

COME ON IN, JOE! THE GAME ALREADY STARTED!

WHAT THE HECK IS GOING ON? YOUR HOUSE IS LIKE A DISASTER AREA, MAN.

OHH, BUCKY BROKE A PLATE BY ACCIDENT AND TRIED TO PRETEND THAT HE DID IT TO "CREATE ART"... NOW HE'S JUST RUINING EVERYTHING HE CAN GET HIS LITTLE PAWS ON... IGNORE IT.

SO... THAT KNEE-HIGH MOUND OF TRASH OUTSIDE THE DOOR IS...

AN "INSTALLATION PIECE."

I HEAR YOU'RE AN ARTIST NOW.

YUP.

TELL ME ABOUT IT.

WELL, I WORK WITH CERAMICS, GLASS, HARD PLASTICS... ANYTHING BREAKABLE, REALLY. I'VE DABBLED IN PAINTING, TOO.

MM-HM.

YOU KNOW—CONDIMENTS, SAUCES, TOOTHPASTE. I PREFER WORKING ON SHAG, BUT I'VE BEEN PRACTICING ON LINOLEUM RECENTLY.

WHERE ARE YOU BOYS OFF TO?

WE HAVE TO GO BUY SOME LIGHTS. SINCE BUCKY TOOK UP ART, THE APARTMENT HAS BEEN PRETTY DARK.

I WORK WITH LAMPS.

OH, FUN! YOU MEAN YOU MAKE AND SELL THEM?

NO, HE BREAKS THEM AND CALLS IT "ART."

HE'S QUITE PROLIFIC.

YOU WANNA KNOW WHY PEOPLE AREN'T GONNA BUY YOUR ART, CAT?

I CAN'T BELIEVE HE LETS YOU DO THAT.

US MC

SCRATCH SCRATCH

YOU'RE JUST TAKING HOUSEHOLD OBJECTS AND BUSTING THEM... IT ISN'T *PRETTY*, SO IT NEEDS TO BE *CONTROVERSIAL*, BUT IT REALLY ISN'T...

IT'S *OFFENSIVE*, THOUGH! THEY'RE *MY* "HOUSEHOLD OBJECTS"!

HMM.

US MC

WELL, I'M RETIRING FROM THE VISUAL ARTS. I HAVE NOTHING MORE TO SAY.

YOU MEAN YOU FINALLY BROKE EVERYTHING YOU COULD REACH.

LACK OF MATERIALS WAS AN ISSUE, YES. ANYWAY, I'VE DECIDED TO BECOME A PERFORMANCE ARTIST. MY FIRST PIECE WILL BE ENTITLED "CAT SLEEPING FOR 22 HOURS STRAIGHT." NOW I MUST GO PRACTICE.

WOW... I THINK I ACTUALLY *LIKE* THIS IDEA...

I HOPE HE GIVES AN INTERMISSION DURING THE PERFORMANCE.

HEY! THERE'S A BIG FISH ON THE FLOOR!

BUCKY, SOME WEIRD CAT IS HERE LOOKING AT YOU FUNNY!

I'M TELLING YOU, I REALLY THINK HE'S SLEEP-WALKING... HE'S BEEN LIKE THIS ALL DAY...

OH, HE'S NOT SLEEPWALKING, HE'S *FREAK*WALKING! **HEY!** ANSWER ME, CAT!

WHO WAS THAT?

MY BOSS. I HAVE TO GO OUT OF TOWN ON BUSINESS.

WHO? ON WHAT?

MY *BOSS*... ON A *BUSINESS TRIP*...I HAVE A **JOB**, YOU KNOW. IT'S WHERE I GO EVERY DAY.

HUH? OH... YEAH. THAT.

YOU SAY "**JOB**," BUT YOU COULD BE GOING **ANYWHERE** FOR ALL WE KNOW. WE TALK ABOUT IT ALL THE TIME.

DAD, I NEED TO ASK A FAVOR...I HAVE TO GO OUT OF TOWN FOR A FEW DAYS AND I WONDERED IF YOU COULD DO A LITTLE PET-SITTING.

YOU MEAN FOR THE **CAT**, TOO?

YEAH...

OH, SEE THAT'S A PROBLEM. I'M ALLERGIC TO CATS.

DAD, YOU'VE NEVER HAD AN ALLERGIC REACTION TO A CAT IN YOUR LIFE.

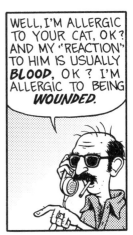

WELL, I'M ALLERGIC TO YOUR CAT, OK? AND MY "REACTION" TO HIM IS USUALLY **BLOOD**, OK? I'M ALLERGIC TO BEING **WOUNDED**.

OK, DAD, I CALLED EVERYBODY I KNOW - **NO ONE** CAN PET-SIT FOR THE GUYZOS...IT'S ONLY FOR A FEW DAYS...

ROBERT...I PUT UP WITH YOU AND YOUR IDIOT BROTHER FOR 25 YEARS, I FOUGHT FIRES FOR 20 YEARS, AND I DID TWO TURNS IN THE WAR...I HAVE *EARNED* THE RIGHT TO **AVOID YOUR CAT**.

WHAT DID HE SAY?

OH, HE'S ALREADY EXCITED...

SLURP!

103

I'M READY TO GO. I GOT MY BLANKIE, MY PILLOW, MR. BONES, A SET OF DISHES, MY—

"DISHES"? YOU'RE ONLY GOING TO BE AT MY DAD'S FOR THREE DAYS.

I FIGURED IN CASE HE DIDN'T HAVE ANY...

MY DAD DOESN'T LIVE IN A *BARN*, SATCHEL, HE DOES ACTUALLY HAVE *DISHES*.

HEY! ...LITTLE *HELP* HERE?!

ONE THING ABOUT LIVING WITH BUCKY- TRY TO *IGNORE* HIS SMACK-TALK, IT'LL MAKE 3 DAYS WITH HIM A *LOT* EASIER.

I DON'T UNDERSTAND WHY YOU DON'T JUST PUT HIM ON SOME SORT OF KITTY PROZAC...

HOLY COW...

SO...YOU'RE VOLUNTEERING TO COME OVER TWICE A DAY AND GIVE HIM A *PILL*?

OK, SEE, YOU'VE OBVIOUSLY THOUGHT THIS OUT MORE THAN I HAVE, I'M JUST THINKIN' OUT LOUD.

THANKS FOR LOOKIN' AFTER THE GUYZOS, DAD. I OWE YOU ONE.

JUST GIVE ME THE LOWDOWN ON THE CAT BEFORE HE GETS BACK...

YOU KNOW BUCKY... JUST KEEP HIM FED... AND *DON'T TOUCH HIS NECK*.

I'M NOT AN *IDIOT*, I'M LOOKIN' FOR *STRATEGY* HERE- LIKE DOES HE ATTACK *STRAIGHT ON*, OR DOES HE SNEAK UP ON YOU FROM *BEHIND*?

HE'S NOT A *SHARK*, DAD.

LIKE *FUN* HE'S N-*AAAEE!*

I WANT TUNA!

OK, HERE'S THE DEAL. I'M NOT GOING TO BABY-SIT YOU, AND I DON'T WANT YOU FOLLOWING ME AROUND BUGGING ME... WHAT'S IT GONNA TAKE TO KEEP YOU OUT OF MY HAIR FOR THE NEXT THREE DAYS?

50 BUCKS AND A TEN-POUND TUNA IN A COOLER.

2 DOLLARS, A CAN-OPENER, AND NO CURFEW.

DONE.

THAT PSYCHO CAT IS **IN THE GARBAGE CAN**, THROWING THE TRASH OUT OF IT **PIECE** BY **PIECE**! I TRIED TO PULL HIM OUT OF IT AND HE **NAILED** ME... I DON'T KNOW IF HE BIT OR SCRATCHED ME, IT WAS ALL A BLUR OF BANANA PEELS, COFFEE FILTERS, AND CAT FUR... AND *THEN* HE HAD THE NERVE TO TELL ME WHEN I COULD GO CLEAN UP! HOW DO YOU *LIVE* WITH HIM?

JOE DOMAN SAYS IT HELPS TO IMAGINE A SOUNDTRACK PLAYING BEHIND HIM... HE SAYS HE IMAGINES THE THEME TO "SHAFT."

HMM... YEAH, I DON'T KNOW IF IT "HELPS"; BUT IT "FITS"...

OF COURSE, I'M NOT ALLOWED TO **WATCH** ANY OF THE MOVIES THAT BUCKY REMINDS THEM OF, SO I WOULDN'T KNOW.

WELL, WELL, WELL. LOOK WHAT THE CAT DRAGGED IN. YOU'VE BEEN GONE OVER 36 HOURS, WHAT ON EARTH HAVE YOU BEEN DOING?

I DON'T HAVE TO ANSWER THAT.

YOU FINALLY RAN OUT OF MONEY, EH?

NO, I STILL HAVE 9 CENTS LEFT, BUT I LOST THE CAN-OPENER. I'M GOING TO SLEEP NOW, IF I'M NOT UP IN 2 DAYS, KNOCK 3 TIMES AND LEAVE SOME FOOD OUTSIDE THE DOOR. GOOD DAY.

DANG. THAT WAS **MY** CAN-OPENER.

I CAN NEVER FIGURE OUT WHERE HE CARRIES HIS MONEY...

107

SO HOW WAS BUCKY TO SIT FOR? DID HE BEHAVE?

HE REALLY WASN'T A PROBLEM. I GAVE HIM A CAN-OPENER AND $2 AND BY THE TIME HE GOT BACK HOME, HE WAS SO TIRED HE SLEPT FOR 2 DAYS. HE JUST WOKE UP NOW, HEARING YOU.

MY KID WENT TO COLLEGE AND ALL I GOT WAS THIS STUPID T-SHIRT.

I DON'T WANT TO **KNOW** WHAT YOU DID, DO I?

HECK, I DON'T EVEN **REMEMBER** WHAT I DID...

YOU WERE MUMBLING ABOUT "ANCHOVIES" IN YOUR SLEEP, BUT I SUPPOSE THAT'S NOTHING NEW.

RUB   RUB   RUB

SO YOU GUYS HAD A GOOD TIME AT MY DAD'S?

YEAH! DID YOU KNOW A **DOG** LIVES NEXT DOOR TO HIM? WE DID TONS OF STUFF. **HE** LIKES "FOOD" AS MUCH AS **I** DO! IT WAS LIKE I'D KNOWN HIM MY WHOLE LIFE...

SATCHEL, WE GO THROUGH THIS EVERY TIME YOU SEE CHOPPER. YOU **HAVE** KNOWN HIM YOUR WHOLE LIFE, YOU JUST NEVER REMEMBER HIM FOR SOME REASON.

I REMEMBER HIM... YOU DON'T FORGET A SMELL LIKE **THAT** WITHOUT THERAPY...

SO DO YOU WANNA **BET** I CAN'T JUGGLE THESE EGGS?

NO, I DON'T WANT TO **BET**, I'M JUST **SAYIN'**, YOU—

BIG TALL GUY CAN'T HANDLE THE PRESSURE, EH?...ALL BIG AND TOUGH UP THERE ON YOUR FREAKISHLY LONG LEGS, BUT CAN'T PUT YOUR MONEY WHERE—

OK, KATT, YOU'RE ON.

SIX SECONDS LATER..

$50...THAT'S LIKE YOUR ALLOWANCE FOR AN ENTIRE YEAR, BIG GUY.

SHUT UP.

BUCKY, YOU HAVE ONE CHANCE TO COME CLEAN WITH THIS...WHAT HAPPENED TO THE SEAFOOD PASTA I MADE FOR MY DATE TONIGHT?

OH...YEAH...I WAS MEANING TO TELL YOU ABOUT THAT...IT WAS...IT WAS, UM, SATCHEL. I TOLD HIM NOT TO EAT IT, BUT HE DID ANYWAY. *"ROB MADE THAT SPECIAL,"* I SAID. BUT HE DIDN'T LISTEN...

YOU'VE GOT SAUCE ALL OVER YOUR FACE, MAN.

darb

UM...HOLY COW, THAT STUPID DOG GOT SAUCE EVERYWHERE...

FUNNY HOW *YOU'RE* THE ONE GETTING GROUNDED, THOUGH.

I DON'T GET THAT CARTOON ON THE FRIDGE.

WELL, SEE WHERE THE "BOSS-GUY" SAYS HIS MOTTO IS "WORK SMARTER, NOT HARDER"? THAT'S *FUNNY.* ... CAUSE IT'S SORT OF INSULTING. AND IT MAKES *HIM* LOOK STUPID.

IT'S SORT OF LIKE *MY* MOTTO.

DO I WANT TO HEAR THIS? ...

"BITE *HARDER,* NOT *FASTER.*"

NOW *THAT'S* FUNNY.

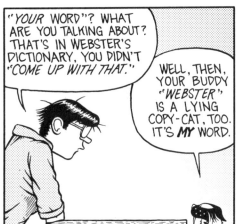

BE BACK BEFORE DARK, ALRIGHT?

OK

LISTEN TO HIM. "OK": ... THAT'S *MY* WORD, *I* CAME UP WITH THAT.

"*YOUR* WORD"? WHAT ARE YOU TALKING ABOUT? THAT'S IN WEBSTER'S DICTIONARY, YOU DIDN'T "COME UP WITH THAT."

WELL, THEN, YOUR BUDDY "WEBSTER" IS A LYING COPY-CAT, TOO. IT'S *MY* WORD.

WHERE DO YOU GET THESE PSYCHO IDEAS?

NOW "*PSYCHO*" IS *TOTALLY* ASSOCIATED WITH ME AND *EVERYBODY* SAYS SO!

SAY SOMETHING FUNNY.

I DON'T DO REQUESTS.

WHAT'S BUCKY BEEN UP TO LATELY? I HEAR HIM BANGING AROUND AT NIGHT, BUT I HAVEN'T SEEN HIM FOREVER.

HE SAID HE WAS GOING TO STAY IN THE GARAGE FOR A WHILE...

WAS HE STILL MOPING ABOUT THAT GIRL WHO WOULDN'T DATE HIM BECAUSE HE'S NOT A FANCY "PERSIAN"?

ODDLY, NO... HE WAS REAL CALM...HE SAID SOMETHING ABOUT A NEW "LOOK" OR SOMETHING.

Rogaine™

A CAT, TWO BOTTLES OF ROGAINE™ LATER...

WE GOT A COMB?

BATHROOM.

?

SO EVEN THOUGH YOU GREW YOUR FUR OUT, THAT PERSIAN WOULDN'T DATE YOU?

SHE SAID I LOOKED LIKE A CHIHUAHUA.

AND ROB YELLED AT YOU WHEN HE SAW IT? HOW ARE YOU GOING TO CUT IT?

HE ONLY YELLED 'CAUSE THE ROGAINE™ COST $80. AND MY ANNUAL BATH IS COMING UP, SO I JUST PUT SOME NO-HAIR CREAM IN THE SHAMPOO.

MEANWHILE...

♪ ♪!

YOU'RE GOING TO SIT IN YOUR CLOSET AND THINK ABOUT WHAT YOU DID.

FIRST YOU YELL AT ME TO CUT MY FUR AND NOW YOU YELL AT ME FOR TRYING TO GET RID OF IT - MAKE UP YOUR MIND!

BUCKY...YOU POURED A WHOLE BOTTLE OF NO-HAIR CREAM INTO MY SHAMPOO. THERE'S **NO WAY** YOU CAN TALK YOUR WAY OUT OF THIS.

JEEZ, YOU JUST GOT THIS TEENY CLUMP OF HAIR ON THE TOP OF YOUR HEAD-WHO KNEW YOU'D BE SO **DEPENDENT** ON IT...

YOU KNOW, USING NO-HAIR CREAM ON YOUR FUR WOULDN'T HAVE JUST "CUT" THE LONG HAIRS - YOU'D BE ALL **NAKED** NOW... YOU'D BE A *SKIN-KITTY*.

WELL, AT LEAST PEOPLE COULD FINALLY HAVE SEEN MY TATTOO.

WHAT?!

NUTHIN'. NEVER MIND. NO TATTOO.

CAN I SEE YOUR HEAD? DOES IT HURT?

NO, THE CREAM JUST MADE IT FALL OUT. I FEEL FINE.

SO... WHAT ARE YOU GOING TO DO?

NOT MUCH TO DO BUT SIT HERE AND LET IT GROW OUT.

WELL...IT'S GOOD TO KEEP BUSY IN THESE DIFFICULT TIMES...YOU JUST KEEP ON GROWIN' IT OUT, ROBBO.

GROWING HAIR ISN'T A "HOBBY," SATCHEL.

RELAX, ROB, IT'S REALLY NOT THAT BAD... *I* USED TO GET MY HEAD SHAVED ALL THE TIME.

YOUR HEAD IS THE SAME TONE AS YOUR *BODY*, MAN. I'M SO WHITE MY SCALP IS *BLUISH*!

GIVE BLOOD PLAY RUGBY

WELL, YEAH... NOW AT LEAST WE CAN SEE THERE ARE NO NUMBERS TATTOOED ON YOUR HEAD.

OH, YOU'RE **SO** FUNNY.

HAHA! YEAH! LIKE *"FOUR"*!

WHAT ARE YOU WATCHING?

YOU KNOW WHAT THAT IS, IT'S A *TV*!

AW, JEEZ, IT'S A PSYCHIC LINE INFOMERCIAL. THIS IS ALL JUST *LIES*, BUCKY.

NO, NO, NO, IT SAYS "FOR ENTERTAINMENT PURPOSES" RIGHT THERE AT THE BOTTOM AND GETTING *LIED* TO ISN'T VERY ENTERTAINING, NOW, IS IT?

MAN-OH-MAN, WHY DO THESE PSYCHIC COMMERCIALS HAVE TO BE 10 MINUTES LONG?

I JUST WANT TO KNOW WHO *FALLS* FOR THIS GARBAGE...

HI. MY NAME IS BUCKY, AND I'M A *"LEO"*..

120

TO GIVE YOU YOUR READING, I'LL NEED TO KNOW YOUR OCCUPATION, MR. BUCKY.

YOU'RE *PSYCHIC*, RIGHT?

OH...YEAH. TOTALLY.

THEN... DON'T YOU KNOW THAT ALREADY?

OH...SURE...I KNOW **ALL** THAT STUFF...I JUST NEED TO SEE IF YOU'RE...UM... BEING **HONEST** WITH ME...

OHHH, GOOD THINKING. WELL, I'M CURRENTLY UNEMPLOYED.

SO, MR. BUCKY, MY UM... SPECIAL "PSYCHIC CARDS" ARE TELLING ME THAT YOU'RE HAVING MONEY PROBLEMS...WHAT WITH YOUR BEING UNEMPLOYED AND ALL...

YES! EXACTLY! I CAN'T EVEN BUY MY OWN TUNA!

WELL, LET'S SEE...OH, GOOD NEWS, THE CARDS SAY YOU'LL GET A JOB VERY SOON...

ARE THE CARDS SURE ABOUT THAT?...A **JOB**? **ME**? OH, NO...THIS IS TERRIBLE...

LADY, ARE YOU SURE THE CARDS SAY I'M GONNA GET A "JOB"? THAT WOULD REALLY CUT INTO MY FREE TIME...I MEAN, I'M ONLY 5...

YOU'RE **5 YEARS OLD**? BUCKY, DID YOU GET YOUR GUARDIAN'S PERMISSION TO CALL OUR PSYCHIC LINE?

ARE YOU CRAZY? HE'D NEVER LET ME CALL A *PSYCHIC*. HE SAYS YOU'RE ALL **CRACKPOTS**...

YOU HAVE TO HAVE PERMISSION TO KEEP TALKING TO ME, DEAR.

THEN, "YES." YES, I DID.

GOOD. LET'S CONTINUE.

SO, BUCKY, YOU'RE 5? WHY DID YOU CALL ME HERE AT *PSYCHIC BUDDIES*? ARE YOU GOING THROUGH A HARD TIME AT HOME?

OH, ALWAYS. I'M CONSTANTLY GETTIN' HASSLED BY "THE MAN"!

DO YOU SPEND A LOT OF TIME ALONE IN YOUR ROOM?

WELL... SORT OF...

OUR **DOG** HAS HIS OWN ROOM, BUT **I** SLEEP ON THE TOWELS IN THE HALL CLOSET... BUT, **YEAH**, I SPEND A LOT OF TIME IN MY CLOSET, SURE.

NOW LISTEN TO ME VERY CAREFULLY, BUCKY, I WANT TO HELP YOU -- ARE YOU TELLING ME YOU'RE 5 YEARS OLD AND EVEN THOUGH THE **DOG** HAS ITS OWN ROOM, YOU SLEEP IN A **CLOSET**?

YUP. ON THE TOWELS.

BUCKY, DO YOU EVER GO TO SLEEP HUNGRY?

ME? OH, NO, NEVER... I SNEAK OUTSIDE EVERY NIGHT AND RUMMAGE THROUGH TRASH CANS... THERE'S ALWAYS *SOMETHING* TO EAT.

BUCKY, CALLING OUR PSYCHIC LINE WAS THE RIGHT THING TO DO... YOU'RE A BRAVE LITTLE BOY, LIVING IN A CLOSET AND EATING TRASH...

THANKS, YOU'RE, LIKE, THE ONLY PERSON WHO REALLY *UNDERSTANDS* ME... MOST PEOPLE JUST MESS UP MY FUR OR PULL MY TAIL...

"FUR"?...*TAIL*"? BUCKY...ARE YOU BY ANY CHANCE A **CAT**?

WOW! HOW DID YOU **KNOW** THAT? OH, RIGHT, YOU'RE *PSYCHIC*, RIGHT... WANDA, IT'S LIKE YOU'RE MY BEST FRIEND!

THAT WILL BE $87.50, CAT.

123

DID EITHER OF YOU CALL A 900 PSYCHIC NUMBER? THERE'S A $90 CHARGE ON MY BILL HERE...

I DID. WANDA WAS AMAZING. I SAID "MY NAME IS BUCKY, AND I'M A LEO," AND SHE TOLD ME EVERYTHING...SHE EVEN TOLD ME **YOU** WOULDN'T BE UNDERSTANDING.

BUCKY, YOU'RE NOT A "LEO." *SATCHEL* IS A "LEO." YOU'RE A "CAPRICORN," MY FRIEND. ...A GOAT.

A...?... A **GOAT**?

MUST NOT LAUGH... MUST NOT LAUGH...

WELL...I GUESS $90 FOR A PSYCHIC ISN'T AS BAD AS THE LAST TIME YOU GOT A HOLD OF MY CREDIT CARD... OR LAST WEEK WHEN YOU BROKE MY ANTIQUE SHIP MODEL...OR *MOST* OF THE STUFF YOU DO WHEN NO ONE'S LOOKING...

I KEEP TELLING YOU! I DIDN'T BREAK YOUR DUMB DINGHY!

HOW DID IT HAPPEN AGAIN? WAS IT A BIG, CRAZY DOG THAT BROKE IN, TOOK IT OFF THE MANTLE AND THREW IT AT YOUR HEAD? YOU'D ACTUALLY BE A *VICTIM* IN THAT SCENARIO...

HMM... THAT **IS** PRETTY GOOD. BUT NO...NO, I STAND BY MY ORIGINAL STATEMENT ABOUT MAD BEAVERS.

I DON'T REALLY LIKE THIS CARTOON THAT REPLACED "PEANUTS"...

IT DIDN'T "REPLACE" PEANUTS, SATCH, IT'S JUST A NEW COMIC... I'LL GO GET YOU ONE OF MY OLD SNOOPY BOOKS.

DID CHARLIE BROWN EVER GET TO KICK THE FOOTBALL?

126

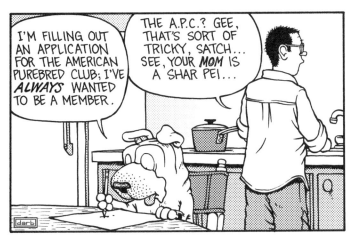

I'M FILLING OUT AN APPLICATION FOR THE AMERICAN PUREBRED CLUB; I'VE *ALWAYS* WANTED TO BE A MEMBER.

THE A.P.C.? GEE, THAT'S SORT OF TRICKY, SATCH... SEE, YOUR *MOM* IS A SHAR PEI...

RIGHT! AND MY DAD IS A LAB! HE WAS A GUIDE DOG!

YEAHH...SEE, THE THING ABOUT THAT IS UM...HMMM... THIS ISN'T GOING TO BE EASY...

OH!...HEY, SATCHEL. WHY ARE YOU SITTING BY THE DOOR? ARE YOU WAITING TO HEAR FROM THE DOG CLUB? YOU JUST SENT THAT APPLICATION YESTERDAY.

YEAH, WELL, MY SCHEDULE IS PRETTY OPEN...

DID I HEAR THE DOOR? OH...IT'S YOU... **HEY,** DID THE MUTT GET HIS REJECTION SLIP, YET?

WHAT DOES HE MEAN?

NOTHING - HE'S JUST BEING WEIRD - BE QUIET, BUCKY.

I'M JUST ASKIN'.

YOU GOT A RESPONSE TO YOUR APPLICATION FROM THE DOG CLUB.

OOO! LEMME SEE!

IT...IT SAYS MY *"BREEDING ISN'T UP TO THE STANDARDS REQUIRED FOR ADMISSION"*...

OUCH.

SO... YOU DIDN'T GET INTO THE AMERICAN PUREBRED CLUB...

NOPE. BUT I'M PROUD TO BE A MUTT.

YOU KNOW, YOU COULD PAINT YOURSELF BLACK AND WHITE AND CHASE SHEEP AROUND AND CALL YOURSELF A BORDER COLLIE...

NAH. I LIKE MY FUR.

SO DO I.

ALL I'M SAYIN' IS IF YOU *REALLY* WANT TO GET INTO THE PUREBRED CLUB, YOU COULD *PRETEND* TO BE SOME *BREED*.

I DON'T *WANT* TO, I *LIKE* BEING PART LAB AND PART WRINKLE DOG. I DIDN'T KNOW "PURE" MEANT, YOU KNOW, "RACIST."

I SUPPOSE IT'S TOO LATE FOR YOU TO LEARN HOW TO HERD SHEEP, ANYHOW..."YOU CAN'T TEACH AN OLD DOG NEW TRICKS"...

YEAH, WELL, "YOU CAN'T TEACH ANY CAT ANYTHING!"

SATCHEL?.... WAS THAT A *COMEBACK*?! *ATTA BOY*! STICK UP FOR YOURSELF!

THAT LETTER YOU'VE BEEN WAITING FOR FINALLY CAME.

FROM THE DOG CLUB? BUT THEY ALREADY REJECTED ME...

OY, *TWO* REJECTIONS. THAT'S HARSH.

NO, NO, IT'S FROM THE PUBLISHER BUCKY SENT HIS MANUSCRIPT TO...

READ IT!

"DEAR MR. KATT, I AM NOT SORRY TO INFORM YOU THAT WE ARE UNABLE TO USE YOUR WORK AT THIS - OR ANY - TIME. WE WILL NOT KEEP YOUR NAME ON FILE. IF YOU AGREE NOT TO SUBMIT MATERIAL IN THE FUTURE, WE AGREE NOT TO FAX IT TO ALL OUR FRIENDS AS A JOKE. I HAVE READ BETTER PROSE ON THE BACK OF A SHAMPOO BOTTLE. SINCERELY, MICHAEL JOHNSON, EDITOR."

WELL... AT LEAST IT'S NOT A "FORM" LETTER.

LEAVE ME.

WOW, ROB, ANY MORE FUR ON THAT COAT AND YOU'RE GOING TO ATTRACT PROTESTERS.

YEAH...MY CAT WAS BEING ALL FUNNY THIS MORNING. DANG... I NEED ONE OF THOSE TAPE-ROLLER THINGS.

AWW, YOU HAVE A FUNNY KITTY? DO YOU HAVE ANY CUTE STORIES YOU COULD TELL?

"CUTE" STORIES?....MY CAT?... OH, NO NO, HE'S NOT FUNNY IN A "HA HA" WAY, IT'S MORE OF A "GOOD LORD NO" KIND OF THING.

SICK, EH? YOU KNOW, GIVING FIVE BUCKS TO A CAT BRINGS YOU GOOD LUCK.

NICE TRY, KITTY.

OK, LET ME REPHRASE THAT: NOT GIVING FIVE BUCKS TO A CAT WILL ALMOST CERTAINLY BRING DISASTER.

HOW 'BOUT I GIVE YOU A $5 CREDIT ON THE RADIO YOU BROKE YESTERDAY...

I KNEW IT! YOU'RE SCRATCHING! YOU HAVE FLEAS!

I'M NOT SCRATCHING! I'M JUST... BRUSHING MY FUR! SEE?....NO SCRATCHING.

GET IN THE TUB. NOW.

I DON'T HAVE FLEAS!

SCRATCH

SCRATCH

134

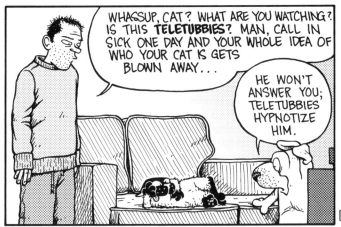

WHASSUP, CAT? WHAT ARE YOU WATCHING? IS THIS **TELETUBBIES**? MAN, CALL IN SICK ONE DAY AND YOUR WHOLE IDEA OF WHO YOUR CAT IS GETS BLOWN AWAY...

HE WON'T ANSWER YOU; TELETUBBIES HYPNOTIZE HIM.

ACTUALLY, HE SORT OF **LOOKS** LIKE ONE OF THEM, DOESN'T HE? SAME DUMPY LITTLE BODY... BIZARRE SPEECH, TOO... HEY, BUCKY COULD BE THE FIFTH TELETUBBY!

HE'D BE "SCRATCHY WATCHY"!

SO, AS YOU KNOW, I'VE BEEN WATCHING A LOT OF DAYTIME TV. ...I FIGURE I MIGHT AS WELL JUST GET MY OWN SHOW.

LYIN' AROUND ALL DAY EATING AND SLEEPING JUST AIN'T DOIN' IT FOR YOU ANYMORE, EH?

WELL, IF YOU'RE GONNA BE *THAT* WAY ABOUT IT...

OK.. I'LL PLAY ALONG...WHAT'S IT GONNA BE..."*MASTERCAT THEATER*"?...."*JUDGE BUCKY*"?

OH! I KNOW! "*WHO WANTS A MILLION SCRATCHES*"!

I'M **SERIOUS**, I'M GOING TO GET MY OWN TV SHOW. I JUST HAVEN'T FIGURED OUT WHAT CHANNEL I WANT TO BE ON.

BUCKY...WHAT ON EARTH MAKES YOU THINK THAT YOU'RE CAPABLE OF HOSTING A TV SHOW?

I'VE BEEN TOLD I'M CHARISMATIC AND THAT PEOPLE RESPECT MY OPINIONS.

BUCKY, THAT WAS A *FORTUNE COOKIE*!

AND YOU MADE ME TRADE WITH YOU 'CAUSE MINE GAVE LOTTERY NUMBERS.

HAVE YOU EVEN THOUGHT THIS OUT? I MEAN, *SURE*, YOU *WANT* YOUR OWN TV SHOW, BUT WHAT WOULD YOU **DO** WITH ONE?

I'M THINKING OF A "HOW-TO" SHOW... YOU KNOW: CRAFTS, INTERIOR DESIGN...

NOW, WOULD THIS BE FOR *EVERYBODY*, OR STRICTLY FOR *CATS*... LIKE SOME SORT OF *FANG SHUI* THING...

WELL, I'LL BE DEALING WITH PLANT DECONSTRUCTION... HOW TO DISTRESS FURNITURE AND SHARPEN YOUR CLAWS AT THE SAME TIME...THAT KIND OF STUFF...SO, YEAH, CATS WOULD PRETTY MUCH BE MY MAIN DEMOGRAPHIC.

FOR THE FIRST PROJECT ON MY TV SHOW, I'M MAKING THIS SAMPLE COFFEE TABLE. I CALL THE STYLE "SIAMESE CONTEMPORARY."

WAIT, YOU DIDN'T *MAKE* THAT. THAT'S **MY** TABLE, YOU JUST GLUED A BUNCH OF **TRASH** TO IT...

WELL, KEEP IN MIND THAT IT DOESN'T HAVE ANY **GLITTER** ON IT YET...WHAT DO YOU THINK?

WHAT DO **I** THINK? I THINK MY MOTHER GAVE ME THIS TABLE AND SHE'S GOING TO WANT TO KNOW WHY WE DESTROYED IT.

YOU COULD TELL HER IT WAS BEAVERS.

I HAD WANTED TO DO A SPANISH TILE MOSAIC ON THIS TABLE, BUT WE DIDN'T HAVE ANY SPANISH TILE, SO I BUSTED UP A MICROWAVE-SAFE PLATE MADE IN MEXICO AND HOT-GLUED IT DOWN.

I LIKE THE RED DESIGN ON THE TILES.

THAT'S NOT A "DESIGN", SATCHEL, IT'S TOMATO SAUCE...BUCKY, YOU'RE SUPPOSED TO WASH FOOD OFF OF STUFF BEFORE YOU MAKE **FURNITURE** OUT OF IT.

ARE YOU PRACTICING HOME DECORATING?

YEAH. I'M "ANTIQUING" THIS PIECE OF FURNITURE.

I DON'T THINK YOU'RE SUPPOSED TO "ANTIQUE" UPHOLSTERY...

DEPENDS ON THE **LOOK** YOU'RE GOIN' FOR.

YOU KNOW...I'VE TRIED TO BE SUPPORTIVE ABOUT YOUR PRACTICING FOR A TV DECORATING SHOW, BUT YOU REALLY HAVE TO BE MORE CAREFUL WITH MY STUFF...I MEAN...I CAN'T EVEN IMAGINE A WORSE MESS THAN THIS.

WELL...IF YOU'RE CURIOUS ABOUT THAT, I SUPPOSE YOU COULD GO LOOK AT THE KITCHEN - THAT'S THE STAGING AREA.

WHAT ARE YOU DOING **NOW**? I TOLD YOU TO STOP WRECKING MY STUFF!

I'M PUTTING A FAUX MARBLE FINISH ON THE VCR.

WHY DON'T YOU TRY MAKING SOMETHING FAUX *TASTEFUL*?

UM...WELL...I LEARNED HOW TO DECORATE FROM TV "HOW-TO" SHOWS, AND THEY NEVER SEEM TO COVER "TASTEFUL."

BUCKY... YOU DON'T KNOW THE FIRST THING ABOUT HOSTING A *CRAFT* SHOW.

IT'S REALLY JUST TAKIN' TRASH AND PAINTING IT. YOU DIG IN A DUMPSTER 'TIL YOU FIND A BUSTED TABLE, SLAP SOME CRACKLE FINISH ON IT, AND GET SOME IDIOT TO *OO*-AND-*AH* OVER IT.

CAN I BE THAT GUY?

YOU'RE NOT GONNA BE BUCKY'S *IDIOT*, SATCHEL!

OF COURSE, IF YOU HAVE A *BUDGET*, YOU CAN TAKE *NEW* STUFF AND MAKE *IT* PAINTED TRASH... AND THEN COVER IT IN GOLD LEAF.

WHAT ON EARTH WAS THAT CRASH?! OHH, *MAN!*

MY BAD.

HEY, CAT, THE CABLE STATION CALLED - DID YOU RESERVE STUDIO TIME TO DO A LOCAL ACCESS PROGRAM WITHOUT ASKING ME?

THAT'S RIGHT, PINKY, I'M GONNA BE A TV STAR - AND IF YOU KNOW WHAT'S WHAT, YOU'LL JUMP ON THE *BUCKY TRAIN* BEFORE IT LEAVES THE STATION...

WELL, THEY ALSO SAID YOU HAVE TO PAY THE PRODUCTION GUY $150 TO DO THE SHOW - HOW DO YOU LIKE *THEM* APPLES, OPRAH?

WHAT? WHAT DO YOU MEAN BY THAT? IT SOUNDS BAD... AND YOU *KNOW* I DON'T LIKE FRUIT...

I'M TELLING YOU YOU'RE WRONG - **REDD FOXX** WAS A **PERSON**!

AAA, WHAT DO YOU KNOW, YOU BIG, PINK, WATER-LOVING FREAK!

I **KNOW** YOU ARE, BUT WHAT AM **I**?

DUDE... DID YOU ACTUALLY JUST **SAY** THAT?

HUH? OH, YEAH, IT'S JUST EASIER TO ARGUE WITH HIM ON HIS OWN LEVEL SOMETIMES.

ARE YOU STILL HERE? SHOULDN'T YOU BE OUT KISSING DOGS OR SOMETHING?

SO... I'VE BEEN THINKIN' ABOUT WHAT NICKNAME I WANT...

YOU WANT? YOU CAN'T **PICK** YOUR OWN NICKNAME, BUCKY, THEY JUST HAPPEN.

WELL, FRANKLY I DON'T TRUST YOU GUYS TO COME UP WITH A GOOD ONE, SO IT'S UP TO ME... NOW IF I WAS A **CANADIAN**, I'D JUST ADD AN *-IE* TO THE END OF MY NAME LIKE "GORDIE" OR "DOUGIE"... SO THAT WOULD MAKE ME...

"BUCKIE."

HMM... YEAH, THAT'S NOT TOO MUCH BETTER, IS IT?

YOU DO REMEMBER THAT "BUCKY" IS ALREADY YOUR NICKNAME, RIGHT? IT'S SILLY TO GET **ANOTHER** ONE, PARTICULARLY WHEN BUCKY SUITS YOU SO WELL.

"SUITS" ME? I DON'T THINK IT SUITS ME AT ALL... IT MAKES NO SENSE.

ARE YOU CRAZY? YOU **DO** KNOW WHY YOU'RE CALLED "BUCKY," DON'T YOU?

WELL... I ASSUME IT'S BECAUSE I'M SUCH A YOUNG **BUCK**, BUT-

WHAT? **NO!** IT'S BECAUSE OF YOUR **TOOTH!** **TOOTH!**

OHHH... HEY, THAT DOES FIT.

143

144

SO THE COMMUNITY ACCESS TV STATION CALLED BACK—YOU HAVE STUDIO TIME RESERVED TOMORROW NIGHT FOR YOUR DECORATING SHOW.

ROCK **ON**. TODAY—OPPRESSED HOUSECAT, TOMORROW—*TV STAR*. I'LL NEED A BIGGER CLOSET, OF COURSE.

YOU'RE DELUSIONAL, YOU KNOW THAT?

WELL, I'M A LITTLE VAGUE ON YOUR *NERD TERMINOLOGY*, BUT IF "DELUSIONAL" MEANS "GORGEOUS," THEN **YES**. YES, I DID KNOW THAT.

SO ARE YOU NERVOUS ABOUT DOING YOUR TV SHOW? LOTS OF PEOPLE WILL BE WATCHING.

HECK NO... I FIGURE IT'S ABOUT TIME THAT I GET SOME RECOGNITION.

"RECOGNITION"?! FOR WHAT?

FOR EVERYTHING THAT MAKES ME SO GROOVY. MY KITTEN-SOFT FUR, FOR EXAMPLE...

MY CAT SENSE TELLS ME THAT MY BEING A TV STAR INTIMIDATES YOU.

NO, THE PROSPECT OF YOU AROUND A MILLION DOLLARS OF ELECTRONIC EQUIPMENT INTIMIDATES ME...

SO YOU'RE INTIMIDATED BY *SOPHISTICATED* THINGS... WELL, YOU CAN STILL HANG OUT WITH **SATCHEL**...

JUST DON'T **TOUCH** ANYTHING IN THE STUDIO.

I DON'T **HAVE** TO TOUCH ANYTHING. I'LL BE THE **STAR**. PEOPLE WILL BE WANTING TO TOUCH **ME**.

THE CAMERA IS BROKEN. YOU'LL JUST HAVE TO TAPE YOUR SHOW LATER... **YOU** DON'T KNOW ANYTHING ABOUT FIXING CAMERAS.

IT'S NOT MY FORTE, NO, BUT I'M SURE I CAN GET IT GOING. IT'S NOT MUCH BIGGER THAN ME...

YOU'RE NOT TRYING TO *BEAT IT UP*, BUCKY, YOU WANT IT TO *WORK*.

GETTING STUFF TO *WORK* IS ALL JUST A MATTER OF DOMINANCE.

HEY, MAN, THAT CAMERA COST $100,000.

'NUFF SAID.

MAN WHAT A DAY...

4F

Wilco

OH, GOOD, YOU'RE HERE, HAND ME THE REMOTE.

TUNA

JUST ONE WEEK I'D LIKE TO BE ABLE TO LIVE *YOUR* LIFE...

HEY, MY LIFE AIN'T ALL WARM CREAM AND DEAD RATS EITHER, MAN.

TUNA

BUCKY, YOU DON'T REALIZE HOW HARD **JOBS** ARE - I SAT AT A DESK FOR **14 HOURS** TODAY, TYPING NUMBERS INTO A COMPUTER! **YOU** LAID AROUND ALL DAY DOING WHATEVER YOU WANTED!

IT'S BEEN A HARD DAY **HERE**, TOO, YOU KNOW - SATCHEL HAD ANOTHER "ACCIDENT" AND I SLEPT THROUGH *EVERY SINGLE ONE* OF MY TV SHOWS!

148

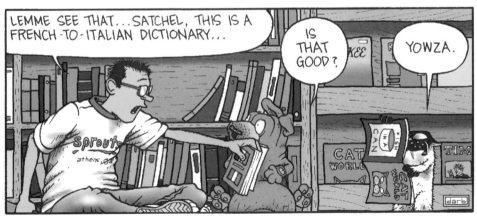

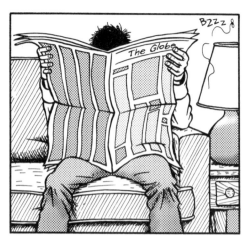

152

I WAS RUMMAGING AROUND IN THE STORAGE ROOM AND I FOUND THIS... CAN I HAVE IT? *OH*, AND WHAT IS IT?

WOW, THAT'S MY OLD COONSKIN HAT. I GOT THAT WHEN I WAS **5**... I GUESS YOU CAN HAVE IT, SURE.

IT'S A *HAT?* HOW DO I LOOK? DO I LOOK "TOUGH"? I WANT TO BE *INTIMIDATING.*

WELL... YOU'RE FREAKIN' *ME* OUT.

COOL.

ARE YOU JUST GOING TO CARRY THAT THING AROUND? IT'S A COONSKIN *HAT*, YOU KNOW, NOT A FUR SECURITY BLANKET.

WELL, IT DOESN'T REALLY *FIT* MY HEAD... BUT YOU THINK IT MIGHT LOOK COOLER THAT WAY?

OK, YEAH, NEVER MIND, JUST KEEP CARRYING IT.

WHAT? DID YOU SAY SOMETHING? IS THIS BETTER? I CAN'T REALLY HEAR ANYTHING. OR SEE...

CHECK IT OUT— THE COONSKIN HAT DIDN'T FIT AS A "HAT", SO I MADE SOME ARMHOLES IN IT AND NOW IT'S A **COAT.** DOES IT LOOK TOUGH? I WANT TO LOOK THREATENING.

BUCKY, YOU LOOK LIKE A BAD GENETIC EXPERIMENT.

SO, YOU ARE, IN FACT, CONFIRMING THAT MY APPEARANCE IS *SCARY?*

ROB, DO YOU KNOW WHERE THE— *AAAAA!*

I KNOW YOU LIKE THAT COON-SKIN THING, BUT IT JUST SEEMS KIND OF MORBID, YOU KNOW... YOU WEARING THE SKIN OF ANOTHER ANIMAL...

AND THAT'S DIFFERENT FROM YOUR LEATHER JACKET *HOW?*

WELL... IT... SEE... WHEN *I*... UM... GO TO YOUR CLOSET.

MAN, THIS IS A CONSPIRACY.

YOU KNOW WHAT? I BET YOU WON'T GET HASSLED BY ANY RACCOONS WHILE YOU'RE WEARING YOUR COONSKIN JACKET!

YOU GOT *THAT* RIGHT, POOCHY.

SO... ROAMING GANGS OF RACCOONS ARE A BIG PROBLEM FOR YOU, EH? WOULD THAT BE HERE DOWNTOWN, OR AT YOUR SUMMER PLACE ON THE VINEYARD?

YOU KNOW, IT JUST SEEMS "WRONG" FOR YOU TO BE WEARING A FUR COAT... EVEN IF IT IS A CONVERTED 20-YEAR OLD COONSKIN HAT.

THE BEAUTY OF WEARING THIS FUR COAT IS THAT IT TELLS PEOPLE I'M TOO *TOUGH* TO CARE ABOUT "ISSUES".

SO... IN YOUR MIND **FUR COAT** MEANS **TOUGH**? NOT ONLY DID *YOU* NOT KILL THAT RACCOON, BUT A **LOT** OF PEOPLE TRY TO *PROTECT* ANIMALS FROM THAT ATTITUDE.

OH, YEAH? WELL, I DON'T SEE ANY TREE-HUGGING HIPPIES JUMPING OUT OF CUPBOARDS TO "PROTECT" *ME* FROM YOUR INCESSANT *WHINING!*

YES! YES!!

WHO'S THE FIERCEST COMPETITOR IN THE *WORLD*, BABY?!

OH! OH! I KNOW! LANCE ARMSTRONG, RIGHT? THIS IS FUN!

CAN I NAME TEAMS? BECAUSE I WOULD SAY THE NEW ZEALAND ALL BLACKS.

...I MEANT ME...I FINALLY CAUGHT THAT BUG UNDER THE FRIDGE...

OH... OK.... **GOOD FOR YOU!**

YEAH, THAT WAS LIKE A HUGE DEAL TO YOU.

SO...I LOOKED FOR MY COMPUTER FOR LIKE AN HOUR AND - *LO AND BEHOLD* - IT WAS IN YOUR CLOSET, WITH PAW PRINTS ALL OVER IT AND A CRACKED SCREEN.

YOU'RE MAD, AREN'T YOU?

GEE, BUCK, HOW'D YOU GUESS?

WE CATS ARE VERY PERCEPTIVE ABOUT STUFF LIKE THAT. *NOW*... TELL ME WHAT YOU'RE MAD ABOUT...

BUCKY, HAVE YOU SEEN THE —

I'M KINDA BUSY STARING AT THIS WALL, SATCHEL.

I JUST HAVE *ONE QUICK QUESTION*—

SATCHEL, *PLEASE!* THE LIGHTING CONDITIONS ARE CHANGING *EVERY SECOND!*

CAN YOU CHECK MY SPELLING HERE? I'M SELLING OFF SOME OF MY COLLECTION - THIS IS THE FLYER I MADE.

UMM...YOU'VE GOT MORE PROBLEMS HERE THAN JUST *SPELLING*, MAN.

WHAT, GRAMMAR? *OH*, IS IT THAT BIG *"SALE"* THING? IGNORE THAT, IT WAS SATCHEL'S IDEA.

IT HAS NOTHING TO DO WITH THE "SALE" THING, TRUST ME.

SALE! FISH HEDZ! NOT LIVE BUT SMELL GUD! NOBODY JUST HED. AL SIZE MUST GO

I HATE THIS MOVIE. WHAT'S WITH THIS STUPID DRIPPING FAUCET? WHY DON'T THEY JUST *FIX* THE DUMB THING?

THE FAUCET IS A METAPHOR, BUCKY.

WAIT...I THOUGHT THE FAUCET WAS A *FAUCET*...

I KNOW THAT; YOU DON'T THINK I *KNOW* THAT? *OBVIOUSLY* IT'S AN...UM... A MELTED FLOWER, *I'M* JUST SAYIN' IT'S DUMB...LOOK AT IT - *DRIP...DRIP... DRIP...DRIP...*

I HAVE TO, UH, "GO OUTSIDE" FOR A MINUTE...

YOUR HAIR IS EVEN FUNNIER SHORT. ESPECIALLY WHEN YOU WAKE UP - IT GETS ALL, YOU KNOW, FLAT AND *MORAL*.

YOU'RE DOING THAT THING AGAIN WHERE YOU USE WORDS INCORRECTLY. IT MAKES YOU SOUND IGNORANT.

I'M NOT "IGNORANT." I WATCH A SOLID 8-HOURS OF CABLE TV A DAY, MAN. I'M *HIGHLY* INTERGALACTIC.

UMM...

NOW THAT'S NOT WHAT YOU *MEANT*, BUT IT IS, IN FACT, TOTALLY ACCURATE.

WHOA, WHOA, WHOA! WHAT THE HECK IS **THAT**? AND WHERE ARE YOU GETTING ALL THIS NEW STUFF?

THIS? IT'S MY... *FAMILY CREST*...IT WAS, UM, A *GIFT*... FROM A LONG-LOST FRIEND... WHO YOU WOULDN'T KNOW...

ANCESTORS WERE KITTEN PIRATES, EH? ARE YOU A DESCENDANT OF *BLACK WHISKER*? WELL, YOU'RE ON YOUR OWN WITH THIS ONE — YOU TAKE THAT ACT OUT IN PUBLIC AND I DON'T KNOW YOU.

ARE YOU SAYING YOU'D LIKE ME TO GO OUT UNSUPERVISED FROM NOW ON?

NOPE. NOT EVEN INTO THE HALL; YOU'RE *DOG BAIT*, MAN.

WHY IS AN EXTENSION CORD GOING INTO BUCKY'S CLOSET?

HOLY COW! WHERE DID ALL THIS STUFF COME FROM?

OH...**HI**... IT WAS, YOU KNOW, UM, *FREE*, FROM AN, UM, STORE.

I'M SUPPOSED TO BELIEVE THAT?

THAT WOULD REALLY HELP ME OUT, THANKS.

OK, FIRST THINGS FIRST — **HOW** DID YOU GET THIS CREDIT CARD?

WELL, THEY SENT ME A "PRE-APPROVED" THINGY, SO I JUST FILLED IT OUT AND SENT IT BACK.

AN APPLICATION? BUT THERE'S A SPACE ON THAT FOR "INCOME".

RIGHT. I PUT DOWN THAT I'D LIKE A MILLION DOLLARS.

THAT'S SUPPOSED TO BE HOW MUCH MONEY YOU HAVE *ALREADY!*

OH... WELL, NO PROBLEM, I CAN GET A CASH ADVANCE.

HELLO? 13th NATIONAL BANK? YEAH, I HAVE A PROBLEM; YOU GAVE MY CAT A CREDIT CARD, AND I NEED TO...... WHAT? ...NO, **I** DON'T HAVE A CARD, MY...WHAT? HOLD ON.

...OK, MY **CAT'S** CARD NUMBER IS 322-4016-6182.

SIR, I SHOW THAT MR. KATT HAS EXCELLENT CREDIT... ALTHOUGH HE IS LATE ON HIS FIRST PAYMENT.

OK, YOU'RE NOT HELPING ME. WHO ELSE CAN I TALK TO?

SEE IF THEY'LL INCREASE MY CREDIT LIMIT.

SO HERE'S THE DEAL: I HAD TO OFFICIALLY DECLARE YOU AS "BANKRUPT" TO CANCEL YOUR STUPID CREDIT CARD DEBTS. ...AND WE'RE RETURNING ALL THE STUFF YOU BOUGHT.

NUTS.

CHEER UP, BUCKY...YOU WANT MY 'MOON PIE'?

DON'T WORRY 'BOUT **ME**, HOMEY, I'LL BE BACK IN THE GAME BEFORE YOU CAN SAY **ALBACORE**.

OH, HEY, SATCHEL, I'LL SELL YOU THIS **'MOON PIE'** FOR $5...

OO! I **LOVE** 'MOON PIES', LET ME GET MY PIGGY BANK!

DUDE, IF HE'S STRONG ENOUGH THAT YOU CAN'T PULL HIM OFF, MAYBE HE DOESN'T NEED AN ANNUAL CHECKUP AT THE VET'S.

YEAH...

YOU GUYS AREN'T HELPING.

162

UNTIL YOU CAN BEHAVE, I WANT YOU TO GO TO YOUR CLOSET.

FOR YOUR INFORMATION, *ROB*, I WAS GOING THERE ANYWAY.

IS THERE A REASON HE WRECKS STUFF? I MEAN, THIS PLANT NEVER DID ANYTHING TO HIM.

WELL, I KNOW HE'S RUDE AND HE EATS WEIRD STUFF AND DOESN'T BATHE, BUT THOSE ARE HIS *INSTINCTS*. BUCKY COMES FROM A LONG LINE OF STUBBORN AND PROUD ANCESTORS.

BUCKY IS *FRENCH?* WELL, THAT STILL DOESN'T EXPLAIN WHY HE —

NO, HE'S A *CAT;* I'M SAYIN' HE'S A *CAT.*

MMM...WARM LAUNDRY...

AAAAAAAAAA

I TOLD YOU NOT TO SLEEP IN THERE!

YYYAWN

AW, JEEZ, THE SEAL ON THIS TUNASNAX BAG IS RIPPED... ALL THE *CHEWINESS* IS GONE! DUMB BAG! YOU'D THINK IF WE CAN PUT A CAT ON THE MOON, WE COULD MAKE A —

BUCKY, THERE'S NEVER BEEN A CAT ON THE MOON.

WHAT?...BUT IT... YOU MEAN...?....I'VE BEEN WORKING ON THAT ASSUMPTION FOREVER. IT...UM... WOW, GIVE ME A SECOND, THIS IS QUITE A SHOCK.

DOGS HAVE BEEN IN SPACE, THOUGH!

WHAT KIND OF BUG IS THIS?

PT!

I BELIEVE THAT WOULD BE AN "EASTERN PANCAKE BUG."

YOU'RE GOING TO TAKE *ANOTHER* NAP?

IT'S NOT A PROBLEM EXCEPT THAT YOU'RE GRUMPY FOR LIKE THE HOUR BEFORE YOU GO TO SLEEP AND THE HOUR AFTER YOU WAKE UP... IT LEAVES LIKE 15 MINUTES A DAY WHEN YOU'RE PLEASANT.

I'D TAKE ISSUE WITH THAT IF I WEREN'T SO SLEEPY.

I'M NOT GONNA EAT THIS.

YOU'RE *GONNA* EAT IT, AND YOU'RE GONNA BE NICE ABOUT IT, TOO. SATCHEL MADE THAT SPECIAL FOR YOU... AND I DON'T SEE *YOU* COOKING ANYTHING.

THE LAST TIME I COOKED YOU COMPLAINED.

SETTING A BOLOGNA SANDWICH ON FIRE IS NOT "COOKING".

IT WAS PRETTY GOOD, THOUGH.

WELCOME... YOU'VE GOT MAIL!

WHAT'S THAT MEAN?

THAT'S MY INTERNET PROGRAM TELLING ME THAT A PERSON SENT ME AN E-MAIL.

OH... WHAT DOES IT SAY IF A **DOG** E-MAILS YOU?

WELCOME! YOU'VE GOT **FLEAS!**

NEXT UP ON THE HOUSE MEETING AGENDA IS READING THE NOTES WE PUT IN THE SUGGESTION HAT THIS WEEK...LET'S SEE, *"I WOULD LIKE THE DOG FOOD THAT MAKES ITS OWN GRAVY"*. FAIR ENOUGH. I'LL ADD THAT TO THE SHOPPING LIST.

ALRIGHT!

OK.. NEXT ONE...HMMM... I DON'T KNOW ABOUT THIS ONE...

WHY? WHAT DOES IT SAY?

READ IT OUT LOUD. THAT'S THE RULE.

SEE... THE HAT IS FOR *SUGGESTIONS*, AND WRITING *"SATCHEL IS A SMELLY FLEA BAG"* IS REALLY JUST AN INSULT.

AW! WHO WROTE THAT?!

I THINK WHOEVER WROTE THAT HAS A VALID OPINION...

CHANNEL 99
COMMUNITY ACCESS
TELEVISION

COME ON DOWN AND WE'LL
GIVE YOU YOUR OWN SHOW.
SERIOUSLY.

HI, WELCOME TO THE **CATHOUSE**, THE CALL-IN SHOW WHERE I SOLVE YOUR HOME-DECORATING PROBLEMS. WITH ME IS MY SIDEKICK *ROBERTO*. HE'S WEARING MAKEUP.

"ROBERTO"? *SIDE*KICK?

look at the camera, Rob.

WELL, FOLKS, WE'RE STILL WAITING FOR OUR FIRST CALL. AGAIN, OUR NUMBER IS 1-555-*CATHOUSE*. THAT'S 1-555-*CATHOUSE*.

OK, I'M GETTING WORD THAT, IN FACT, OUR NUMBER IS **NOT** 1-555-*CATHOUSE*, SO YOU'LL ALL NEED TO STOP CALLING THAT. APPARENTLY, I JUST ASSUMED IT.

LET'S GO TO THE PHONES. YOU'RE ON THE AIR, CALLER, DO YOU HAVE A HOME-DECORATING QUESTION?

HELLO?... I CAN'T REACH THE LIGHT SWITCH... IT'S DARK AND SCARY... HELLO? IS ANYBODY THERE?

SATCHEL?

OK, LET'S KEEP THE CALLS **ON TOPIC**, PEOPLE, AND NO CRACK-POTS; WE HAVE CALLER I.D.

BUCKY? HELLO? *ROB?*

USE THE STOOL, SATCHEL! THE **STOOL!**

From the Rejected Character File:

#40: Vichy, the Chain-Smoking French Poodle

HELLO, CALLER, DO YOU HAVE AN INTERIOR DECORATING PROBLEM I CAN HELP YOU WITH?

UH...YEAH, I HAVE A SPARE CABINET DOOR THAT I CAN'T USE, BUT I DON'T WANT TO THROW IT AWAY...

MM-HM, MM-HM. I WOULD PAINT IT GOLD, HAMMER SOME LEGS ON IT, AND CALL IT A COFFEE TABLE.

WELL...I GUESS I COULD DO THAT...IT'S GOT A BUSTED HINGE ON IT, THOUGH...

OH, BROKEN HINGES ARE *VERY* "COLLECTIBLE" RIGHT NOW. PAINT IT GOLD, HANG IT ON THE WALL, AND TELL PEOPLE HOW GREAT IT IS BEFORE THEY CAN FORM THEIR OWN OPINION ON IT.

UNH.

SO...YOU'RE SAYING I CAN HANG A BROKEN DOOR HINGE ON THE WALL AS "ART"?... I DUNNO...

ARE YOU QUESTIONING ME?! I'M THE **HOST** OF THIS SHOW, PAL! YOU DON'T—

SETTLE DOWN, BUCKY.

"SETTLE DOWN"? *"SETTLE DOWN"?!* EASY FOR **YOU** TO SAY, PINKY, **YOU** AREN'T DEALING WITH THESE IDIOTS! IF I HEAR ONE MORE STUPID—

CUT, CUT, CUT.

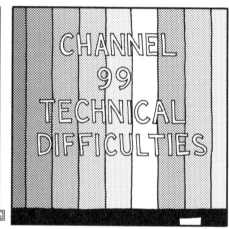
CHANNEL 99 TECHNICAL DIFFICULTIES

I'M JUST SAYIN' YOU SHOULDN'T HAVE CALLED YOURSELF A "PROFESSIONAL" INTERIOR DECORATOR ON T.V....I MEAN YOU'VE NEVER BEEN *PAID* FOR IT.

SATCHEL PAID ME.

YEAH, I GAVE HIM SOME PAINT AND A DOLLAR TO PAINT MY WALL.

YOU MEAN YOU GAVE HIM A CAN OF PAINT, HE MADE THAT MESS IN YOUR ROOM, AND THEN YOU *PAID* HIM FOR DOING IT?

UM...YEAH. I ADMIT IT DOESN'T SOUND SO GOOD WHEN YOU SAY IT OUT LOUD...

MAYBE YOU'RE NOT AS CRAZY AS I THOUGHT.

SSSH.

174

I'LL HAVE A CAN OF TUNA.

THIS IS A CHINESE RESTAURANT, BUCK.

MA'AM, WHAT IS THIS ONE?

THAT'S THE "FAMILY PLATTER."

I'LL EAT CHINESE TUNA; I'M NO RACIST.

SORRY ABOUT THIS... WE DON'T GET OUT MUCH.

WOW, THAT'S MADE FROM A WHOLE FAMILY?

I DON'T WANT "CHUNG DUNG FOO," OR WHATEVER, I WANT TUNA.

BUCKY, *YOU CHOSE* THIS PLACE! NOW WHEN THE WAITRESS COMES BACK, I WANT YOU TO KNOW WHAT YOU WANT.

HM.

I KEEP SAYIN'— I WANT *TUNA*.

YOU HAVE TO PICK SOMETHING OFF THE **MENU**.

GUYS, LOOK! WHO AM I? "*I WANT TUNA! I WANT TUNA!*"

I'D LIKE YOU TO LOOK AT THE FIGURE ON THIS PAPER.

OK....WHAT IS IT?

THAT'S HOW MUCH I WANT YOU TO RAISE MY ALLOWANCE.

...AND JUST WHERE DID YOU COME UP WITH THIS —*RATHER LARGE*— FIGURE?

OH, I DO MOST OF MY QUALITY THINKING IN THE OL' SANDBOX.

OK, TOO MUCH INFORMATION.

179

WHAT'S WRONG WITH YOU? YOU'RE USUALLY IN A PRETTY GOOD MOOD WHEN YOU GET BACK FROM DUMPSTER DIVING AT THE FISH MARKET... I MEAN, IT'S ALL *RELATIVE*, BUT...

I GOT TAUNTED BY A **RABBIT** IN THE PARK, WITH TONS OF CHICKS AROUND... HE WAS ALL **FOOFY**, BUT THERE WERE LIKE A *MILLION* OF 'EM... LAUGHIN' SO HARD AT ME THAT GRASS WAS COMIN' OUT OF THEIR NOSES.

SOUNDS LIKE YOU HAD ONE OF THOSE *"BAD HARE DAYS."*

TERRIBLE HARE DAY.

I PLEDGE ALLEGIANCE, TO THE CAN... OF THE PERFECT FOOD THAT IS TUNA. AND TO THE FISHY, FOR WHICH IT CANS, ONE PORTION... JUST FOR ME, WITH OLIVE OIL, AND CRACKERS, ON TOP.

HEY, DO YOU SMELL THAT? IT'S LIKE...OH, BUCKY IS HERE.

YEAH, NO OFFENSE, BUT YOU REALLY REEK, BUCK.

WELL *SATCHEL'S* NOT ONE TO TALK, HE SMELLS LIKE A *BASSET HOUND.*

WOW, REALLY? A "BASSET"? **ME**? I'M NOT EVEN DOING ANYTHING NEW...

THAT'S A COMPLIMENT TO HIM, YOU KNOW.

YEAHHH, I REALIZED THAT AS I WAS SAYIN' IT...

HI, ROB, YOU LEFT YOUR CASE IN MY CAR THIS AFTERNOON.

OH, HEY, JOE, THANKS.

...WHAT?

DUDE, YOUR CAT'S BREATH IS REALLY, REALLY FOUL.

ODOR IS JUST ONE OF THE WEAPONS IN MY OVERALL PROGRAM OF DOMINANCE AND INTIMIDATION.

YEAH, IT'S A PROBLEM.

SERIOUSLY, BUCKY, YOUR BREATH IS REALLY BAD. YOU SMELL LIKE A HOT BUCKET OF **CHUM**... I THINK IT'S TIME WE GET YOUR TEETH CLEANED.

MAYBE WE OUGHT TO CLEAN YOUR **HEAD**...BIG DIRTY HEAD...

ROB, I LIKE IT...IT REMINDS ME OF LOW TIDE.

YOU'RE COMPLETELY INCAPABLE OF HAVING A DISCUSSION WITHOUT GETTING RUDE. DO YOU KISS YOUR MOTHER WITH THAT MOUTH?

NO, BUT I'LL BITE **YOU** WITH IT.

CAN'T WE ALL JUST GET ALONG?

HEY, SATCHEL- WHAT'S BLACK AND WHITE AND **RUDE** ALL OVER?

BUCKY!

I HEARD THAT!

WHAT IS THIS? WHAT ARE YOU WATCHING?

IT'S THE OLYMPIC HIGHLIGHTS SHOW.

WELL, I'M HERE NOW AND I DON'T LIKE IT. GET RID OF IT.

BUT SYNCHRONIZED DIVING IS NEXT...

OK, NOW YOU GUYS ARE BEING SYNCHRONIZED ANNOYING; GIVE ME THE REMOTE!

NO! GET OFF!

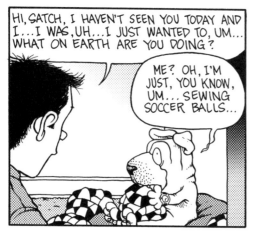

HI, SATCH, I HAVEN'T SEEN YOU TODAY AND I...I WAS, UH...I JUST WANTED TO, UM... WHAT ON EARTH ARE YOU DOING?

ME? OH, I'M JUST, YOU KNOW, UM...SEWING SOCCER BALLS...

THOSE ARE "SOCCER BALLS"? MAY I ASK WHY YOU'RE MAKING SOCCER BALLS?

SEE... THE THING IS... I'M NOT SUPPOSED TO TELL YOU ABOUT—

BUCKY!

BUCKY, PUT SMACKY DOWN; I WANT YOUR ATTENTION- ARE YOU MAKING SATCHEL SEW SOCCER BALLS FOR YOU?

SATCHEL'S "WORKING" FOR ME, YES. MANUAL LABOR ISN'T REALLY A "CAT" THING.

PEOPLE AREN'T GONNA BUY THEM, BUCK, THEY'RE NOT REAL SOCCER BALLS!

OH, LIKE A BUNCH OF SWAN-DIVIN', SHIN-GRABBIN', MAMMA'S BOYS ARE GONNA KNOW THE DIFFERENCE.

OH, MY HEAD... THIS CAN'T BE HAPPENING.

NO, NO, SERIOUSLY, HERE'S MY CATALOG.

184

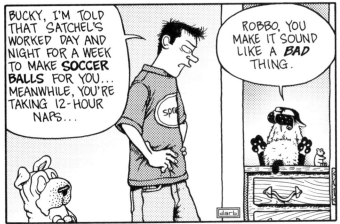

BUCKY, I'M TOLD THAT SATCHEL'S WORKED DAY AND NIGHT FOR A WEEK TO MAKE **SOCCER BALLS** FOR YOU... MEANWHILE, YOU'RE TAKING 12-HOUR NAPS...

ROBBO, YOU MAKE IT SOUND LIKE A **BAD** THING.

BASICALLY, YOU'RE RUNNING A ONE-DOG **SWEAT SHOP.**

WELL, I DON'T KNOW ABOUT **THAT**... SEE, TECHNICALLY, DOGS' DON'T "SWEAT," SO IT'S REALLY MORE OF A "**PANT**" SHOP."

LOOK - THE BOTTOM LINE HERE IS THAT I'M PAYING SATCHEL THE SAME SALARY THAT OTHER DOGS GET IN THIS AREA...

WELL...I'M NOT TRYING TO "COMPLAIN," BUT YOU HAVEN'T PAID ME ANYTHING YET...FRANKLY, IT'S BEEN VERY BAD FOR MORALE...

WHAT DO YOU HAVE TO SAY TO THAT, BUCK?

WELL SURE, FORTUNATELY FOR ME, THE GOING RATE FOR DOG SALARIES AROUND HERE HAPPENS TO BE "NOTHING."

YOU KNOW WHO YOU ARE? YOU'RE **KITTY LEE GIFFORD.**

CATCHIN' SOME OF THE LAST WARM RAYS OF THE SEASON, EH, BUCKY?... *YEAHHH*, I'M DOWN WITH THAT... AYUP... *I* HEAR YA...

SO, YOU ACTUALLY THOUGHT YOU COULD **SELL** THESE "SOCCER BALLS" AND MAKE SOME MONEY?

WHY NOT? OTHER COMPANIES DO IT.

BUCKY, YOU'RE NOT A "COMPANY"; YOU'RE A CAT... YOUR ONE "EMPLOYEE" WAS A STRESSED-OUT DOG WITH A SORE PAW AND LOW MORALE.

YEAH, BUT HE WAS WORKING FOR FREE.

I GUESS THE LARGER ISSUE IS WHETHER YOU'RE NUTS OR JUST PLAIN STUPID...

WELL, **I'M** NOT TELLIN'.

OK... I'M SENSING THAT YOU'RE NOT HAPPY WITH MY SOCCER BALL FACTORY - **NO BIG DEAL** - I CAN SLOW DOWN PRODUCTION. I DON'T THINK YOU NEED TO SEND ME TO MY CLOSET.

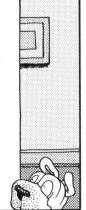

BUCKY, YOU DON'T GET IT, DO YOU? YOU MADE SATCHEL WORK FOR A **WEEK** ON A SCHEME TO MAKE **YOU** MONEY... DO YOU EVEN HAVE ANY **IDEA** WHAT LEVEL OF TROUBLE YOU'RE IN?

ARE YOU LETTING ME SUGGEST A LEVEL?

SORRY, NO.

CAN'T YOU AT LEAST THANK SATCHEL FOR DOING ALL THAT WORK FOR YOU?... ...JUST SAY "**THANK YOU, SATCHEL!**"

YOU'RE PUSHING YOUR LUCK TODAY, KITTY... HOW WOULD YOU LIKE TO BE GROUNDED FOR YOUR ENTIRE LIFE?

GO NUTS, I GOT **NINE** OF 'EM.

NOW, I WANT YOU TO THINK ABOUT WHAT YOU DID TO SATCHEL. AND REMEMBER - YOU NEVER FOOL ME... YOU ALWAYS JUST GET IN TROUBLE LIKE THIS.

I FOOL **SATCHEL**, THOUGH.

OH **WHOOP-DEE-DOO**, DO YOU WANT A **MEDAL** FOR... OH... SORRY, SATCHEL...

THAT'S OK.

WOULD THIS "MEDAL" HAVE ANY MONETARY VALUE?

YOU HAVE A LOT OF SILVER FUR NOW... YOU USED TO BE A SOLID *SEAL* POINT...

I HAVE "HAIR." **YOU** HAVE "FUR."

SNOB.

WHOA... THIS UNDERWEAR YOU'RE BUYING WAS MADE BY **SATAN!**

$TUFF Mart

THEY'RE NOT MADE "BY SATAN," THEY'RE MADE "OUT OF SATIN."

OH... YEAH, THAT MAKES MORE SENSE... HEY, **FANCY**.

HA! HA! THEY WOULD HAVE BEEN UNDERPANTS FROM THE UNDERWORLD! ...**HOT** PANTS!

191

BUCKY, WHY DON'T YOU **DO** SOMETHING? YOU KNOW, GET OUT AND GET SOME EXERCISE...

OHHH, I DO **PLENTY**, MY FINE, TWO-LEGGED FRIEND. YOU HAVE NO IDEA OF ALL THE SUBTLE INTRICACIES OF CATHOOD. YOU SEE, BEING A **CAT** MEANS YOU LIVE A LIFE OF INTRIGUE AND SECRECY.

OH SECRET, *SHMECRET* — YOU WAKE UP, EAT, TAKE A NAP, EAT *AGAIN*, AND THEN PLAY WITH A RUBBER BAND IN THE MIDDLE OF THE NIGHT BEFORE YOU GET UP AND DO IT ALL OVER AGAIN.

WAIT, YOU... YOU **KNOW** ABOUT THE "RUBBER BAND" THING?

BUCKY, THE **WORLD** KNOWS ABOUT YOUR RUBBER BAND THING.

SOMETIMES YOUR CRASHING AROUND KNOCKS MY PET ROCKS OFF THEIR SHELF.

BUCKY HAS HIS COSTUME ON!

HOWDY.

HA HA! *NICE!* WHAT MADE YOU WANT TO BE A COWBOY?

WELL, IT WAS EITHER THIS OR A *FIREMAN*, AND THEN I REMEMBERED THAT COWBOYS GET TO PUNCH DOGGIES.

OK, *NOT* SO NICE.

DO COWBOYS REALLY DO THAT, ROB? DO THEY REALLY?

COME ON, SATCHEL, GET YOUR COSTUME ON! WE'RE GONNA BE LATE FOR THE PARTY!

WHAT THE HECK ARE YOU?.... A *VACUUM CLEANER?*

YEAH...IT WAS THE SCARIEST THING I COULD THINK OF.

EXCELLENT COSTUME, DUDE, *VERY* SCARY.

dirt devil

run away!

YOU'RE STILL WEARING YOUR COSTUME AROUND? HALLOWEEN IS OVER, BUCK.

HALLOWEEN MAY BE OVER, MY FRIEND, BUT *STYLE* NEVER GOES OUT OF... UM...STYLE.

SO YOU GOT "STYLE" RECENTLY, EH? GOOD FOR YOU. I MUST HAVE MISSED THAT.

ROB, ROB, ROB. YOU DON'T *GET* STYLE; YOU EITHER HAVE IT OR YOU DON'T.

SO...UNLIKE "FLEAS", FOR EXAMPLE, YOU CANNOT *ACQUIRE* "STYLE":...

CORRECT. STYLE IS AN *ATTRIBUTE*, WHEREAS "FLEAS" ARE MORE OF AN *ACCESSORY*... AND A RATHER LOW-CLASS ONE, I MIGHT ADD.

SO YOU'RE SAYIN' THAT YOU'RE STYLISH ENOUGH TO BE ABLE TO WEAR THAT COSTUME YEAR-ROUND, HUH?

I WAS **BORN** WITH STYLE, MAN. AND THIS OUTFIT HAPPENS TO SUIT MY SIGNATURE RUGGEDNESS PERFECTLY.

I GET IT. YOU'RE EITHER BORN WITH STYLE OR YOU'RE NOT.

THAT'S RIGHT. AND FORTUNATELY FOR ME, I'M **COMPLETELY** INBRED WITH IT.

HEYYY, THERE'S THE LITTLE COWBOY! NO, WAIT, YOU'RE OUR LITTLE COW**CAT**! OR ARE YOU A DANGEROUS OUTPAW? YOU KNOW, A **DESPERWEIRDO**!

NO, NO, HE'S A **TUNA WRANGLER**! AN **ALBACOREBOY**!

OH '**HAR-DEE-HAR-HAR**,' YOU GUYS ARE SO FUNNY I CAN'T STAND IT...OH, NO, HOLD ON - IT'S **YOU GUYS** I CAN'T STAND!

WHOA, YOU GUYS ARE OUT OF CANDY ALREADY?! HALLOWEEN WAS JUST TUESDAY!

MAYBE WE COULD WHACK SATCHEL WITH A STICK AND SEE IF WE GET MORE.

LOWE TECH

TRADER JOE'S

THAT'S A **PIÑATA**, MAN, YOU CAN'T JUST **WHACK** SOMETHING AND GET **CANDY** OUT OF IT!

HE ATE A **TON** OF CANDY, I'M JUST SAYIN' MAYBE WE CAN GET SOME **BACK**.

YOU CAN'T GET CANDY OUT OF SATCHEL, BUCKY.

WELL...MAYBE IF WE HIT HIM **LONG** ENOUGH, HE'LL **BUY** US SOME CANDY.

I FEEL ILL...

THINGS THAT GO BUMP IN THE NIGHT...

HEY, BUCK, DID I GET A PACKAGE TODAY? I'M WAITING FOR A NEW PALM ORGANIZER FOR -- AW, **MAN!** WHAT ARE YOU DOING?!

THIS ISN'T WHAT IT LOOKS LIKE.

YOU'RE SITTING NEXT TO AN OPEN PACKAGE WITH AN ORGANIZER IN YOUR DIRTY, LITTLE PAWS... HOW COULD IT **NOT** BE WHAT IT LOOKS LIKE?

OH, YOU **SAW** THE ORGANIZER? OK, THEN YEAH, THIS IS WHAT IT LOOKS LIKE.

A-HA! YOU'RE NOT THE ONLY ONE WHO HAS A FANCY DIGITAL ORGANIZER! FEAST YOUR EYES ON **MY** NEW TOOL!

THAT'S SATCHEL'S OLD **GAMEBUDDY**, MAN.

I SEE. WELL, THAT EXPLAINS WHY IT WAS TRYING TO BLOW ME UP AS I WAS ENTERING MY DATA...

SO... THIS IS A **GAMEBUDDY**, NOT A "PALM PILOT"? BUT I SPENT ALL THAT TIME INPUTTING MY SCHEDULE TO IT... GOOD THING I **REMEMBERED** TO NAP TODAY; I COULD HAVE BEEN **REALLY TIRED** OTHERWISE.

HANG IN THERE, BUCKY!

AND DO US ALL A FAVOR: **WHEN IN DOUBT, NAP.**

"WHEN IN DOUBT..." BY JOVE, THAT'S **BRILLIANT!**

WELL, YOU FINALLY BROKE SATCHEL'S GAMEBUDDY... I DON'T KNOW WHY YOU CAN'T JUST LEAVE STUFF ALONE... I MEAN, WHAT'S YOUR *PROBLEM?*

THE VET SAID IT WAS "BEHAVIORAL," BUT I PREFER TO THINK OF IT AS "GENETIC"... IT CUTS DOWN ON LIABILITY.

I'M SORRY THAT BUCKY BROKE YOUR GAMEBUDDY, SATCH. WE CAN GET YOU ANOTHER ONE, IF YOU—

NO, NO, I DON'T WANT ONE... NEVER USED IT... I'M NOT A BIG FAN OF ELECTRONIC STUFF, YOU KNOW? *BEEPS... BEEPS* FREAK ME OUT. THEY'RE BAD... *MOST* TECHNOLOGY IS BAD.

WHOA, DUDE, CALM DOWN, YOU SOUND LIKE YOU LIVE IN A CABIN IN THE WOODS.

HEY! THERE'S *NOTHING* WRONG WITH LIVING IN THE WOODS!

SATCHEL'S THE *UNABARKER*.

ROB, THIS IS SATCHEL, FROM THE OTHER ROOM... BUCKY DIDN'T MAKE THAT MESS IN THERE, **I** DID... **SATCHEL**... BUCKY TRIED TO **STOP** ME, ACTUALLY...

UM... THAT'S NOT ME SAYING THAT...

WE'RE FLYING TO MY MOM'S FOR THANKSGIVING, GUYS. YOU TWO WILL HAVE TO SHARE A SEAT ON THE PLANE, OK?

HOW *FUN!*

SLURP!

ISN'T BUCKY JUST *PRECIOUS?!* AND HE'S SO *BIG* NOW! LOOK AT HIS BELLY!

YEAH, HE'S BEEN PACKING ON THE OL' *OUNCES* THIS YEAR.

HE EATS BUTTER.

OH, I JUST WANT TO *BOOP* HIS LITTLE NOSE!

OK, YOU'RE GONNA WANT TO FIGHT THAT URGE, MOM.

BUCKY, WHY DON'T YOU GET TO KNOW MY MOM'S CAT WHILE I HELP OUT IN THE KITCHEN. HER NAME IS BUTTERCUP, AND BE NICE- SHE'S SHY.

HEY, BABY, WHAT'S-

NOW YOU LISTEN TO ME, YOU FOREIGN FLEA FACTORY- YOU STINK UP *ANY PART* OF MY HOUSE AND I'LL TURN YOU INTO *TENDER VITTLES.* CAPISCE?

I HATE BEING AT THE LITTLE TABLE.

AREN'T YOU GONNA EAT, CHEWIE? IT'S THANKSGIVING!

I'M JUST WAITING FOR YOU GUYS TO FINISH SO I CAN EAT ALL THE BONES AND GRISTLE.

OHHH...KAYYY...

I MEAN, AS LONG AS YOU GUYS ARE **COOL** WITH THAT. *NO RUSH*...

SO DID YOU GUYS HAVE A GOOD TIME AT MY MOM'S?

YEAH!

YOUR RELATIVES ARE WACKOS.

BUCKY, IF YOU SO DISDAIN PEOPLE, WHY ARE YOU ALWAYS HANGING AROUND?

I ASSURE YOU—MY INTEREST IN PEOPLE IS PURELY CULINARY. AFTER ALL, IT WAS THANKSGIVING. EVERY ONE OF THOSE WACKOS HAD TURKEY...

LOOK! ROADKILL...

HEY! IS ANYBODY THINKING WHAT *I'M* THINKING?

OHHH, I DOUBT IT...

I'VE NOTICED THAT YOU GUYS HAVEN'T BEEN CALLING ME BY THE NICKNAME WE ALL AGREED TO.

HAVE YOU ALSO NOTICED HOW SILLY IT WOULD BE TO CALL YOU "SHIRLEY"?

HEY MAN, "SHIRLEY" IS A GROOVY NAME. BUT I *HAVE* BEEN THINKING THAT I'D LIKE AN EVEN *TOUGHER* NAME...LIKE A *RAP STAR*.

LIKE *LL FOOL J*?...OR *PUBLIC ENIGMA*?

OR *FLUFF* DADDY!

OOO, THAT ONE IS PRETTY GOOD...

YOU ALRIGHT IN HERE? YOU SOUND LIKE YOU'RE HACKIN' UP A LUNG...

NO-NO-JUST A HAIRBALL... OCCUPATIONAL HAZARD FOR A CAT. EVERYTHING'S COOL NOW, THOUGH. NOTHING TO SEE HERE.

WHY ARE YOU STILL WEARING THAT COSTUME HOLSTER AROUND? YOU KNOW YOU AREN'T ALLOWED TO PLAY WITH TOY GUNS...

I DON'T *HAVE* A GUN, I CARRY SMACKY IN IT.

OH. WELL, THAT'S OK. THERE WAS JUST SOMETHING PARTICULARLY UNSETTLING ABOUT A *CAT* PACKIN' A GUN.

HE'S PACKIN' SMACKY.

YES, THAT'S CORRECT.

BUCKY, DID YOU PUSH THE "SELF-CLEAN" BUTTON ON THE OVEN? AND IF SO, *WHY*?

YES. IT WARMS UP THE KITCHEN.

THE FROZEN PIZZA WAS IN THERE DEFROSTING, MAN.

OH. HMM. WELL, SATCHEL WILL STILL EAT IT.

YEAH, I'LL EAT IT.

WHAT'CHA READING?

IT'S A BOOK ABOUT "STRING THEORY"; I DOUBT YOU'D BE INTERESTED IN—

PLEASE. I KNOW *EVERYTHING* ABOUT STRING. I *AM* A *CAT*.

NO, MAN, NOT—

HOMEY, I COULD **WRITE** THAT BOOK: "CHAPTER ONE—YARN. CHAPTER TWO—TYING STUFF TO IT..."

Dr. Brian C. Adair

'MORNING. ≥yawn≤

WHOA, WHAT THE HECK HAPPENED TO YOU?

SCRATCH

SCRATCH

Bucky

WHAT DO YOU MEAN? I'VE BEEN *SLEEPING*... WHAT DO YOU THINK I DO, PLAY "PIN-THE-TAIL-ON-THE-DONKEY" ALL NIGHT?

HEY, WHAT YOU DO IN YOUR OWN BEDROOM IS NONE OF MY BUSINESS.

sprout

Bucky

SATCHEL, DID A REP FROM THE AUTO INSURANCE AGENCY CALL TODAY? I'M WAITING FOR A CUSTOMIZED QUOTE.

MM-HM MM-HM

SO DID THEY OUTLINE LIABILITY ISSUES AND QUOTE SEPARATE FIGURES FOR COMPREHENSIVE AND BASIC COLLISION?

MM-HM. MM-HM.

SATCHEL...DO YOU HAVE ANY IDEA WHAT I'M TALKING ABOUT?

NO...BUT I'M ENJOYING HANGING OUT.

BUCKY, WE CAN'T PUT THE HEAT UP ANY HIGHER – APART FROM THE *COST* OF HEATING OIL, YOU HAVE TO CONSIDER THE *ENVIRONMENT.* YOU KNOW? *GLOBAL WARMING.*

GLOBAL WARMING, GLOBAL *SCHWARMING!* I'D SETTLE FOR A LITTLE *APARTMENT WARMING* RIGHT ABOUT NOW...

WHERE IS "GLOBAL"? YOU SAY IT'S WARM THERE? MAYBE WE SHOULD GO THERE...

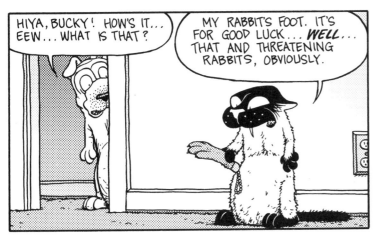

HIYA, BUCKY! HOW'S IT... EEW... WHAT IS THAT?

MY RABBIT'S FOOT. IT'S FOR GOOD LUCK... *WELL*... THAT AND THREATENING RABBITS, OBVIOUSLY.

OHHH, THAT MUST BE WHAT ROB IS TALKING ABOUT WHEN HE SAYS *"BUCKY AND ALL HIS FAUX PAWS."*

ACTUALLY, THERE'S JUST THE *ONE*.

WHATCHA DOIN'?

I'M WORKING ON AN AD CAMPAIGN. IT MAKES ME FEEL LIKE DIRT AND I HATE IT...IT'S CALLED "*BRANDING*." YOU HAVE TO CREATE AN *IMAGE* FOR SOMETHING.

OH, LIKE HOW "SATCHEL" IS A "SISSY."

THAT'S NOT AN "IMAGE", THAT'S AN "*OPINION*."

AND NO HE'S NOT!

OK, SO YOU'RE INSISTING THAT IT WASN'T YOU THAT RIPPED OPEN THE CHRISTMAS SALMON... FUNNY, 'CAUSE *SATCHEL* IS THE ONLY OTHER PERSON IN THE HOUSE.

YOU THINK IT WAS HIM TOO, EH?

TINTIN

SEE... IT'S REALLY MORE THE KIND OF THING **YOU** WOULD DO...

OH, YOU KNOW HIM, HE'S INTO WHATEVER **I'M** INTO.

WHAT ARE YOU GUYS --- EEW, RAW FISH, YUK.

TINTIN

STOP FIDGETING WITH YOUR COLLAR AND **DO** IT...LET'S GO, MISTER. I DON'T HAVE ALL DAY. OUR COMPANY WILL BE HERE SOON AND I WANT YOU TO LOOK "NICE."

HO HO

OK, NOW THE OTHER ONE; COME ON.

WHAT'S IN THE BAG, DUDE?

THE DOCTOR SAID I NEEDED TO USE IT.

HOLY COW!... IS IT THIS SERIOUS?! YOU COULD *DIE* USING THIS!

DON'T YOU THINK I KNOW THAT?!

ANIMAL TOOTHPASTE
- SAFE FOR DOGS AND CATS
- LIVER FLAVOR

IT'S FRIDAY NIGHT, DUDE; WE SHOULD BE DOING **SOMETHING**.

HEY, YOU WANNA GO TO "FLAT-TOPS"?

YEAH, I HAVEN'T PLAYED BILLIARDS IN AGES! BACK IN COLLEGE, I WAS QUITE THE *POOL SHARK*, REMEMBER?

WAS IT A DIFFICULT TRANSITION FROM THAT TO *TOILET WEASEL*?

GO TO YOUR CLOSET.

WAIT... YOU'RE A *WHAT*?

GUYS...WE HAVE TO TALK...

WHAT'S WRONG? WHAT HAPPENED?

I DIDN'T DO IT.

"AN-I-MAL TOOTH-PASTE"... **WOW!** JUST LIKE PEOPLE!

OF COURSE YOU KNOW THIS MEANS WAR.

AHH, THE LAST NUT... LONELY LITTLE FOOD, YOUR LONG JOURNEY IS NEAR AN END...

YOU SPENT MANY MONTHS GROWING ON A SUNNY HILLSIDE IN A FAR-OFF LAND. THEN, ONE DAY, YOU WERE AT LAST PICKED AND SENT MILES AND MILES HERE; WHERE YOU ARE NOW THE LAST OF YOUR NUT BRETHREN.

ALL THIS JUST SO I... I CAN... UM...

CRUNCH CRUNCH CRUNCH

WHAT'S THE MATTER WITH YOU? YOU'RE ACTING PARTICULARLY WEIRD...

SSH. I'M JUST KEEPING AN EYE ON THE FISH.

THE FISH IN THE FRYING PAN? IT'S DEAD, MAN.

I'M NOT GONNA FALL FOR **THAT** ONE AGAIN. ...*DON'T STAND IN FRONT OF IT!* I NEED TO BE ABLE TO SEE IT AT ALL TIMES! THIS IS ALL ABOUT **TACTICS!**

SO... YOU'RE SAYING THAT YOU'RE NOT GOING TO LET A DEAD FISH OUTSMART YOU.

NOT IF I CAN HELP IT.

I WROTE SOME STAND-UP MATERIAL; YOU WANT TO HEAR IT?

"COMEDY"? SERIOUSLY? YOU? YEAH, GO NUTS.

UM, OK, GOOD EVENING... SO *DOGS* ARE PRETTY DUMB, EH? ...AND *UGLY.* THANK YOU, YOU'VE BEEN GREAT - MY NAME IS BUCKY AND I'LL BE HERE ALL WEEK.

YOU'LL NEED MORE THAN THAT, BUCK.

THERE'S PLENTY MORE WHERE THAT CAME FROM.

I DON'T GET IT.

BRIGHT LIGHTS, BAD KITTY.

CHECK IT OUT, SATCH, A LATE PRESENT CAME FOR YOU IN THE MAIL!

OOO, I LOVE LATE PRESENTS!

HEYYYY! IT'S A NEW "MR. BONES"!

OH BOY, HERE COME THE WATERWORKS.

MAN, HE'S NOT GONNA CRY OVER A CHEW TOY.

I KNOW HE'S NOT GONNA "CRY," HE'S GONNA DROOL ALL OVER EVERYTHING!

BUCKY, HOW MANY TIMES HAVE I TOLD YOU NOT TO MESS MY CLOTHES UP?! I HAVE A MEETING THIS MORNING AND MY PANTS ARE COVERED IN CAT HAIR!

OH, SURE, BLAME THE CAT! THAT'S SUCH A CHIPMUNK MENTALITY.

I'M JUST SAYING THAT... UM... YOU NEED TO... TO UHH... WHAT DID YOU JUST SAY?

I SAID CHIPMUNK AND I MEANT CHIPMUNK!

I CAN'T BELIEVE YOU SAID THAT...

IF THEY EVER MAKE A STATUE OF ME, I'M GONNA POSE LIKE THIS.

WON'T THAT JUST GIVE PIGEONS MORE PLACES TO SIT ON YOU?

HMM... YEAH, THAT'S NO GOOD.

MAYBE YOU COULD TELL THEM YOU WANT A PLAQUE!

YOU KNOW, I JUST REALIZED THAT YOU SHOULD BE *PAYING* ME FOR WHEN I CLEAN THE LITTERBOX.

SURE. AND YOU CAN REIMBURSE *ME* FOR ALL YOUR FOOD AND THE STUFF YOU WRECK.

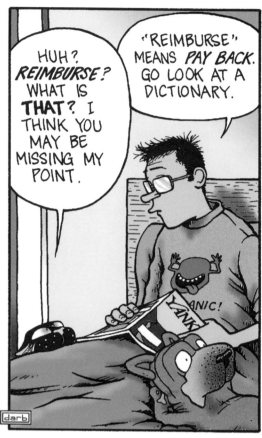

HUH? *REIMBURSE?* WHAT IS *THAT?* I THINK YOU MAY BE MISSING MY POINT.

"REIMBURSE" MEANS *PAY BACK.* GO LOOK AT A DICTIONARY.

DIKSHA-*WHAT?* OK, **NOW** YOU'RE JUST MAKIN' UP WORDS TO STALL ME!

HERE'S A WORD FOR YOU: *NUTJOB!*

WAIT... *I* CLEAN HIS LITTER-BOX...

YOU GUYS WANT TO SEE ME SAW SATCHEL IN HALF? I JUST LEARNED HOW TO DO IT.

OOO! A TRICK! YEAH!

AND WHEN DID YOU LEARN *MAGIC*, BUCKY?

LEARN WHAT? OH...YEAH... "*MAGIC*"..

OK, IS THIS AN ACTUAL "*MAGIC TRICK*", OR JUST SOME WARPED, LITTLE "*CAT FANTASY*"?

OK, OK, OK, I GOT A *REAL MAGIC* TRICK THIS TIME — WANNA SEE IT?

YEAH!

HMMM.

OK...I'LL NEED A 20-DOLLAR BILL. AND YOU'LL BOTH HAVE TO CLOSE YOUR EYES.

JUST GO GET MY PIGGY BANK... I'LL WAIT HERE.

OK, I SEE WHERE YOU'RE GOING WITH THIS.

YOU KNOW... IT'S LIKE YOU'RE *PROUD* OF THESE LITTLE MESSES... LIKE YOU EXPECT *PRAISE* FOR MAKING THEM...

NO, NO — I'LL GIVE YOU AN *AWARD*! TODAY'S AWARD FOR "BEST USE OF A FOOD AS A FLOOR COVERING" GOES TO BUCKY KATT, FOR HIS MOVING PIECE "*WHAT I ATE FOR BREAKFAST*"!

MAN, TV IS SO PREACHY.

DUDE... THIS IS THE *WEATHER FORECAST*... SHE'S TELLING YOU THE *WEATHER*.

"WEAR CLOTHES, DON'T DRIVE IN THE SNOW - DO THIS, DON'T DO THAT"... I *GET IT* ALREADY, MISHELLE!

HEY, SATCH. HOW WAS YOUR DOG GROUP? AND WHO WERE YOU JUST TALKING TO? NEW FRIEND?

UM...YEAH. HE'S OK...HE PLAYS A LITTLE ROUGH, THOUGH, AND HE'S SO BIG...

IS HE A GREAT DANE?

WELL... HE'S AN *ACCEPTABLE* DANE, I GUESS.

"GREAT DANE"... *THERE'S* AN OXYMORON FOR YA.

COME ON, GUYS, WE HAVE TO GET GOING!

BUCKY IS LYING ON THE FLOOR... HE WON'T COME...

WELL, JUST PICK HIM UP AND LET'S *GO!*

BUT...HE'S LYING POINTY-SIDE UP...

HEY, BUCK, YOUR BIRTHDAY IS COMING UP AND I JUST THOUGHT I'D ASK YOU IF THERE WAS SOMETHING YOU NEED...

BABOON REPELLENT.

...EXCUSE ME?...

A CAN OF BABOON REPELLENT... YOU HAVE TO BE READY FOR THEM... THEY ATTACK WHEN YOU LEAST EXPECT IT.

I'M SORRY... I HAD NO IDEA YOU LIVED IN FEAR OF THAT.

WELL, YOU KNOW WHAT THEY SAY - AN OUNCE OF PREVENTION IS WORTH A POUND OF CURE.

NOBODY WHO SAYS THAT IS REFERRING TO BABOON ATTACKS, BUCKY.

IF YOU WON'T GET ME A CAN OF BABOON REPELLENT FOR MY BIRTHDAY, CAN I HAVE A GOLDFISH?

LEMME THINK ABOUT THAT.

NO.

YOU DIDN'T REALLY "THINK ABOUT THAT"!

TRUST ME - I'VE BEEN THINKING ABOUT THAT POSSIBILITY YOUR WHOLE LIFE.

DOES THAT HAVE ANYTHING TO DO WITH HOW YOU USED TO WAKE UP SCREAMING 'NOT THE FISH! NOT THE FISH!'?

SO CAN'T YOU THINK OF ONE THING YOU'D WANT FOR YOUR BIRTHDAY?

THE REAL QUESTION IS, "WHY DON'T I GET GIFTS ALL THE TIME?" IT'S A WELL-KNOWN FACT THAT CATS ARE SUPERIOR TO EVERYBODY ELSE. SEEMS LIKE YOU GUYS OUGHT TO BE SHOWERING ME WITH GIFTS CONSTANTLY.

I'M TRYING TO GET YOU A GIFT. WHY DO YOU HAVE TO BE SO DOGMATIC?

WHAT DID YOU JUST CALL ME?

"DOG-O-MATIC"?

HMM...BUCKY, THIS BOOK SAYS YOUR AGGRESSION MAY BE AN ATTEMPT TO GET *ATTENTION*... IT SAYS YOU MIGHT HAVE AN INFERIORITY COMPLEX AND A "FEAR OF REJECTION WHICH STEMS FROM DEEP-SEATED ABANDONMENT ISSUES."... HM. WHAT DO YOU THINK ABOUT THAT?

"THIS CAT WILL REACT WITH HOSTILITY AND/OR VIOLENCE WHEN DISCIPLINED OR CONFRONTED WITH ITS BEHAVIOR."...SEE? IT'S ALL IN HERE!

DID I JUST HEAR THE PHONE RING?

YUP. AND FOR FIVE DOLLARS I'LL TELL YOU WHO IT WAS.

WHAT? WAS IT FOR ME? CUT IT OUT, BUCKY, YOU'RE BEING MEAN. WHO WAS IT? WAS IT MY MOM?

TELL YA WHAT-FOR A DOLLAR I'LL GIVE YOU HIS **INITIAL**.

...SO IT'S A "*HE*"!

HUH? OH... YEAH, DARN... ANYWAY, THIS **ANONYMOUS** PERSON'S INITIAL IS "*G*" OR IS IT "*J*"?... WAIT, WHAT DOES "*JOE*" START WITH?

DUDE, IT HELPS TO BE SMART IF YOU'RE GONNA BE MEAN.

BEEP BOOP

..."*GOE*"?...

231

233

THANKS FOR TAKING THE GUYZOS WHILE I'M AWAY, DAD.

YEAH, NO PROBLEM. IT WASN'T TOO BAD LAST TIME, SO WHAT THE HECK.

OK, BUCK, I'LL SEE YOU IN A FEW DAYS. BE GOOD, OK?.... ...OK?

TALK TO THE PAW.

MAN, I HATE IT WHEN HE PICKS UP ANNOYING LITTLE "POP CULTURE" THINGS.

ESPECIALLY WHEN THEY'RE ALREADY "OLD."

FRANCIS, DID YOU GET A CHANCE TO LOOK AT THAT LIST OF STUFF I NEED? I'M REALLY GONNA NEED THAT SINGING FISH PLAQUE A.S.A.P.

YEAH, I LOOKED AT IT.

WELL... HERE'S A REVISED COPY, JUST IN CASE.

OK, THANKS. AND HERE'S THE FIRST COPY WITH SOME LITTLE SKETCHES I ADDED OF MYSELF LAUGHING AT YOU.

I LIKE THE BOTTOM ONE BEST, YOU LOOK SO HAPPY.

POW·MIA

THIS **IS** THE LINE FOR THE HYDRANT, RIGHT?

YEAH.

THAT IDIOT DOG FROM NEXT DOOR IS IN THE HALL... I CAN SMELL HIM.

HEY NOW, CHEWIE IS COOL. YOU'RE JUST *ANTI-DOG*.

NO, NO, I HAVE NOTHING AGAINST DOGS *PER SE*...

UH-OH, HERE IT COMES.

I MEAN, SOME OF MY BEST FRIENDS ARE "DOGS".

OY.

BUCKY, THAT'S LIKE A LIE..... NO...NO, THAT *IS* A LIE...

SO FOR DINNER, I'D LIKE A TUNA SANDWICH, 8 FISH NUGGETS, A TUNA CASSEROLE WITH SARDINE GARNISHES, AND A WARM BOWL OF CREAM.

OH, AND I DON'T COOK, SO YOU'LL PROBABLY WANT TO GET GOIN' ON THAT PRETTY SOON.

OK, LISTEN UP, CHEF *BOY-AR-DUM*, NOBODY *"COOKS"* IN THIS HOUSE, CAPISCE? I'M ORDERING A PIZZA, AND IF YOU'RE **GOOD, I'LL GET ANCHOVIES ON IT, GOT IT?**

HA HA! "CHEF BOY-AR--"... UM.. ...UHHH... HA HA! *"CHEF"*!

FRANCIS, I'M GOING-

NO.

BUT I WANT TO-

NO.

IN ANCIENT EGYPT, CATS WERE-

OH, WOULD YOU SHUT UP ABOUT THAT ALREADY?!

BUCKY?... BUCKY? ARE YOU AWAKE?

KNOCK KNOCK KNOCK

I HAD A BAD DREAM...I COULDN'T WAKE ROB UP...COULD I SLEEP WITH YOU?

YEAH, YEAH, YEAH — PULL OUT A DRAWER AND SHUT UP.

THANKS.

YOU KNOW WHAT? I THINK MY WATCH ISN'T WORKING...

SATCHEL, THAT THING HASN'T MOVED IN AGES.

DO YOU THINK IT COULD HAVE BEEN ONE OF THOSE "TIME CHANGE" THINGIES? I MEAN, IT STILL SHOWS A TIME...

DUDE, THAT WAS FOUR MONTHS AGO.

LET'S SEE... YEAH, THAT WAS ABOUT WHEN THE LITTLE HANDS STOPPED...WOW, SO THAT WAS IT?

NO, SATCHEL, IT...OH, NEVER MIND. YES. YES, IT WAS THE "TIME CHANGE THINGY".

HEY, BUCK, I HAVE TO RUN OUT AND...AND... ARE YOU ACTUALLY WATCHING "TEMPTATION ISLAND"? WHAT THE HECK FOR?

IT...IT'S GIVING ME A PAIN IN A TINY LITTLE AREA IN MY SKULL. I'M TRYING TO FIGURE OUT WHAT'S GOING ON...

THAT TINY AREA IS YOUR BRAIN, MAN.

UMM... YYYEAH... YEAH, THAT SOUNDS RIGHT.

WANNA HEAR A JOKE? HUH?... ROB?... OK, "HOW MANY HUMANS DOES IT TAKE TO CHANGE A LIGHTBULB? ... JUST **ONE** IF IT'S TRAINED WELL..."

BUCKY... I DIDN'T LAUGH THE *FIRST* FIFTY TIMES YOU TOLD THAT JOKE, WHY DO YOU *KEEP* TELLING IT?

I FIGURE SOONER OR LATER, YOU'LL **GET** IT.

YOU KNOW WHAT I JUST REALIZED? ...I DON'T THINK THAT BUCKY HAS EVER **MADE** OR **LAUGHED** AT A JOKE...NOW THAT I THINK ABOUT IT, HE'S NEVER LAUGHED AT **ANYTHING**...

HOW ABOUT THAT TIME HE WAS TRYING TO TICKLE ME ON THE FERRIS WHEEL? HE WAS PRETTY HAPPY THEN...

DUDE, HE WASN'T TRYING TO *TICKLE* YOU, HE WAS TRYING TO *PUSH YOU OFF!*

OH... OH MY... WELL, IT DID *TICKLE*...

MAIL!

THANKS.

WHAT?! WHO IS THAT FROM?! IT LOOKS ALL **GOVERNMENTY!** WHO IS IT FROM?!

...AND YOUR MAIN FEAR OF THE GOVERNMENT IS...?...

WELL, **CLONING,** OBVIOUSLY! I MEAN **LOOK** AT ME...I'M *GORGEOUS!*

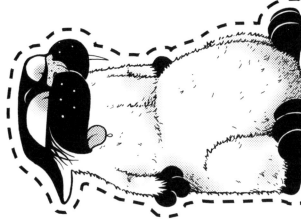

- JUST CUT IT OUT ALONG THE DOTTED LINE, PIN IT TO YOUR WALL, AND WATCH IT DO... *NOTHING!*

JUST LIKE A REAL CAT!

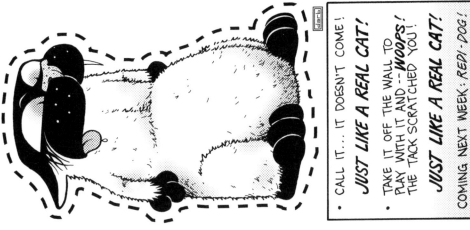

- CALL IT... IT DOESN'T COME!

JUST LIKE A REAL CAT!

- TAKE IT OFF THE WALL TO PLAY WITH IT AND -- *WOOPS!* THE TACK SCRATCHED YOU!

JUST LIKE A REAL CAT!

COMING NEXT WEEK: *REDI·DOG!*

I *LOVE* MUSHY PORK!

IT'S "MOO SHOO" PORK.

THE FOOD FORMERLY KNOWN AS "PIG."

I HAVE TO RUN INTO THE STORE AND GET SOME SNACK FOOD, OK?

HOW IS THAT DIFFERENT FROM REGULAR FOOD?

YOU KNOW- JUST LITTLE STUFF. NOTHING TOO FILLING.

OHH, OK. LIKE CHIPMUNKS. WHY DIDN'T YOU JUST SAY-

I MEAN LIKE *PRETZELS.*

AHH, I SEE MY LIST OF IDEAS FOR EXOTIC NEW FOOD PRODUCTS HAS CAUGHT YOUR EYE.

EWW... BUCKY, NOBODY WOULD EAT THIS STUFF... "RATS 'N' BRAN"..."FROG TARTS"..."MICE-A-RONI"... THESE ARE VILE.

WELL, KEEP IN MIND THEY'LL BE TARGETED TO ONLY THE MOST SOPHISTICATED CARNIVORES' PALETTES.

"I CAN'T BELIEVE IT'S NOT OTTER" IS "SOPHISTICATED"?

MMM, "GEESE'S PIECES"!

HOW DO I KNOW YOU'RE NOT JUST TRASHING MY FOOD IDEAS BECAUSE YOU THINK THEY'RE **GENIUS** AND YOU WANT TO SELL THEM YOURSELF?

YOU COULDN'T SELL THESE AS "FOOD" IF YOU WANTED TO... "QUAKER INSTANT GOATMEAL"?... "CHIPMUNKS AHOY!"...THESE ARE ILLEGAL, LET ALONE INSANE.

YOU KNOW WHAT THEY SAY: "THERE'S A FINE LINE SEPARATING GENIUS AND INSANITY."

YOUR LINE MUST BE PERFORATED, MAN.

HEY! YOU'RE UP WHILE IT'S STILL LIGHT OUTSIDE! HOW WAS YOUR SLEEP?

SCRATCH SCRATCH

I DON'T REMEMBER... I WAS PRETTY OUT OF IT...

244

KNOCK KNOCK.

WHO'S THERE?

"BUCKYBROKE"...

...BUCKY BROKE **WHAT?**

BUCKY BROKE YOUR COMPUTER... SORRY, THERE WAS NO REAL "FUN" WAY TO TELL YOU.

I'M NOT GONNA BUY YOU "PET FISH", BUCKY. STAND THERE ALL YOU WANT, BUT YOU'RE JUST BEING A PEST.

I **KNOW** I AM, BUT WHAT ARE **YOU**... WAIT... THAT'S NOT RIGHT...

From **FUZZCO** it's
REDI-DOG!

FREE to a good home

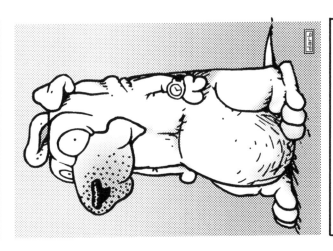

- NO YARD?
- NO EXTRA TIME ON YOUR HANDS TO COMMIT TO "RESPONSIBLE" PET OWNERSHIP?

MAYBE A *FAUX* FIDO IS THE DOG FOR YOU!

- JUST CUT IT OUT AND ENJOY THE BENEFITS OF DOG OWNERSHIP WITHOUT ALL THE INCONVENIENCES!

- IT'S AS EASY AS *SNIP SNIP SNIP,* AND IT'S THE ONLY "OPERATION" *THIS* DOG REQUIRES... ANOTHER PLUS!

SO I SPENT THE ENTIRE DAY WATCHING SOAPS, LIKE EVERYBODY TALKS ABOUT.

I GOTTA TELL YA, I DON'T KNOW WHAT THE BIG DEAL IS.

WHICH ONES DID YOU WATCH?

WELL...THE DISH DETERGENT, MOSTLY, BUT I DID CATCH SOME OF THE ZEST BAR IN THE TUB...

DUDE...

OK, SO YEAH, THE BUBBLE ON THE DETERGENT NOZZLE WAS PRETTY COOL, I GUESS, BUT AFTER IT POPPED...HEY... NOTHIN'!

WHOA. WHAT WAS THAT?

WHAT'S WHAT?

DIDN'T YOU HEAR THAT CRASH? IT SOUNDED LIKE A BOOKCASE FALLING...

I'VE LEARNED TO IGNORE THAT KIND OF THING.

"HEAR NO EVIL, SEE NO EVIL, SPEAK NO EVIL", EH?

DUDE, IN THIS HOUSE, I'M SATISFIED WITH "*SMELL* NO EVIL"...

CAN YOU SPELL "LITIGATION" FOR ME? I'M WRITING A, UM, "LETTER".

JUST DON'T TELL ME WHAT IT'S FOR...

DANG, YOU'RE A BIGGER IDIOT THAN SATCHEL IS...THIS IS JUST A BUNCH OF-

YOU'RE HOLDING IT UPSIDE-DOWN, BUCKY.

SESAME STREET LOOKS SO FUN... I'D LOVE TO GO THERE.

ME TOO.

YOU HATE SESAME STREET.

THAT DOESN'T MEAN I DON'T WANT TO GO THERE.

FOR THE LAST TIME -- BIG BIRD IS, LIKE, **HUGE!** IF YOU TRIED TO EAT HIM, HE'D FLATTEN YOU!

YOU DON'T **KNOW** THAT.

WHAT'S THIS BOAT BROCHURE THINGY?

MY OFFICE IS DOING THE ADS FOR A CRUISE LINE... THAT'S THE, UM, BROCHURE... THINGY.

HEYYYY, THIS IS *FANCY.* IT HAS AN ENTIRE POOP **DECK.**

OH, GREAT, IT'S A **DOG** BOAT.

MAYBE I CAN....... **NO.** NO, I CAN'T USE THAT.

ASK NOT FOR WHOM THE SMELL ROLLS- IT ROLLS FOR THEE.

I'M CHANGING YOUR DIET, MAN.

FEEL... DIZZY...

OOPS, I GOT SOME DROOL ON MYSELF... AND THE RUG... AND HEY, I WONDER WHAT THAT DRIED FOOD IN MY FUR WAS.

DON'T YOU EVER GET TIRED OF BEING A DOG?

HEY, GRENDEL, HOW'S THE MARKET?.... MM-HM... I *TOLD* YOU - WHEN TUNA HITS 79, YOU *BUY! BUY! BUY!*

GIVE ME MY CELL PHONE BACK, BUCKY. AND STAY OUT OF MY BRIEFCASE.

ROBBO, I *NEED* THIS PHONE - YOU DON'T WANT PEOPLE TO THINK I'M SOME CLUELESS LOSER LIKE SATCHEL, DO YOU?

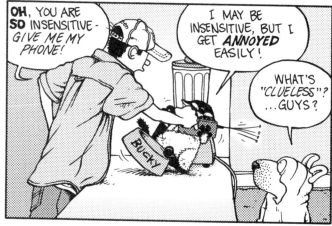

OH, YOU ARE **SO** INSENSITIVE - *GIVE ME MY PHONE!*

I MAY BE INSENSITIVE, BUT I GET *ANNOYED* EASILY!

WHAT'S "*CLUELESS*"? ...GUYS?

251

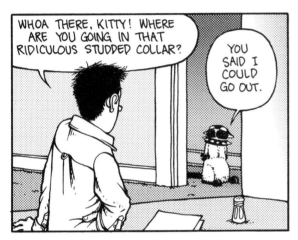

OH! CHOCO BLOCS! GIVE ME ONE!

SORRY, NO MORE CHOCOLATE FOR YOU GUYS. SATCHEL GOT REALLY SICK THE LAST TIME HE ATE IT.

I HAD A RUMBLY IN MY TUMBLY.

ON THE OTHER HAND, *I* CAN EAT IT UNTIL MY PANTS BUST. BUT *HEY*, DOES KITTY WANT A RICE-BASED, ANTI-PLAQUE TREAT?

DON'T PATRONIZE ME.

I'LL EAT IT...

HEY, WOW, YOUR PEAS ARE REALLY GREEN. HEY, HAVE YOU EVER LOOKED AT YOUR PAW? I MEAN **REALLY** LOOKED AT YOUR PAW? HEY, DID YOU HEAR ABOUT THE NEW TRASH CANS DOWNSTAIRS? HEY, I'M GONNA LOOK OUT THE WINDOW...

CATNIP?

OH, MAN, ALL DAY.

THIS DOCUMENTARY IS SO STUPID. "PUMA" IS PRONOUNCED *POOMA*, NOT *PYOOOMA*.

OH, RELAX, *BOOOKY*.

HA HA! *BOOOKY*!

KOTTKE
SANDERS THEATER CAMBRIDGE